TO FREIDA,

HERE'S [barcode: D1196443] ENJOYABLE
FREE T OU CAN
SIMPLY RELAX NJOY!

THANKS FOR YOUR
SMILING SUPPORT!

Zalman Goldstein

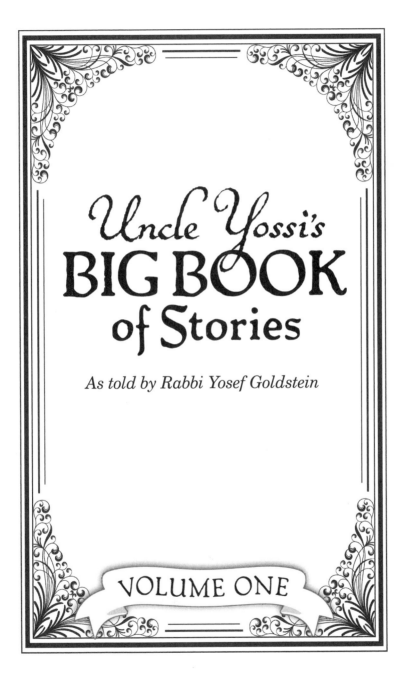

Uncle Yossi's
BIG BOOK
of Stories

As told by Rabbi Yosef Goldstein

VOLUME ONE

Uncle Yossi's Big Book of Stories
Volume 1

Copyright © 2014
by Zalman Goldstein

THE
JEWISH
LEARNING GROUP

Tel. 1-(888)-56-LEARN
www.JewishLearningGroup.com
Email: Info@JewishLearningGroup.com

ISBN-13: 978-1-891293-44-3

Table of Contents

About Uncle Yossi

For over forty years, "Uncle Yossi" has been a household name in Jewish homes around the world. A legend amongst youngsters, master educator and storyteller, Rabbi Yosef Goldstein, has inspired generations of children through his stories and songs conveyed in a wholesome and captivating manner, teaching the eternal ethics and morals of our people and heritage.

Carefully blending stories, parables, and tales drawn from the Torah, Talmud, and Midrash, he instilled a love of G-d, love of the Torah, and love of the Jewish people, while inspiring fine character development and personal refinement. From the first release of what was to become an ongoing series, his recordings were eagerly welcomed in homes across the spectrum.

As the youngest of his ten children, I am grateful for having merited the opportunity to observe my father practice his craft throughout my childhood years, and for the great honor of being able to share with you more of his wisdom and warmth through this collection of his stories as transcribed from his recordings.

May G-d reward my father generously for all the good he has done and inspired, and may his memory be for a blessing.

Zalman Goldstein

The Two Voices

It is Shabbos afternoon, and little Sarah had just finished her Shabbos meal and is on her way over to her friend's house to review some of her Hebrew studies.

As she is walking along, she notices a coin lying on the ground. She comes closer and sees that it is a dime. It was at this moment when it all began. For just as she was standing there looking at the dime, she suddenly heard a voice calling:

"Sarah, Sarah! Pick up that dime, Sarah! Pick it up. Don't just stand there and look at it! You can buy yourself some delicious candy with ten pennies!"

Sarah turned around but saw no one. "Who are you? Where are you? I can't see you!"

"Never mind that, Sarah. Just do what I'm telling you to do. Pick up that dime!"

"But... but it's Shabbos today, and I'm not allowed to handle any money. That would be an awful sin!"

"How foolish, Sarah. It's only a dime. It's just a little sin. What's wrong in doing just a little sin? Come on, Sarah, pick it up!"

Now, Sarah remained standing there. She was a bit confused. She just couldn't make up her mind.

As she stood there, staring at the dime, she again heard another voice calling:

"Sarah, don't listen to that voice. That is the *Yetzer Hara*, the little voice that tells you to do bad things. Don't listen to him. Just keep on walking. Hurry, hurry, your friend is waiting for you. Hurry Sarah, you're on your way to learn Torah. Hurry, hurry..."

Sarah called out, "Then you must be the *Yetzer Tov*, the voice that tells me to do good things."

"That's right, dear Sarah. Don't listen to the other voice. You know it is Shabbos today, and you're not allowed to touch that dime. Remember, Sarah, there is no such thing as a little sin. Every sin is bad. Hurry, Sarah! Hurry, hurry Sarah!"

Now, this went on and on and Sarah just couldn't decide what to do. At that moment, her father came along and noticed how she was standing and looking down at the sidewalk.

"What's the matter, dear Sarah?" he asked. "Don't you feel well? And why that puzzled look on your face?"

Sarah pointed to the dime and began to cry. After wiping the tears from her face, she looked up to her father and said, "Daddy, is it wrong to do a small sin?"

Her father looked at her. "Why Sarah, I'm surprised at you. You know better than that. Of course, it's wrong to do any kind of a sin. In fact, there's no such thing as a small sin."

Saying this, Father took Sarah over to a bench and they both sat down and he said to her, "Let me explain it to you, dear Sarah. In fact, I'll tell you a story, and from the story you will understand clearly what I'm trying to teach you."

Sarah always loved to hear stories, and especially from Daddy. She looked up to her father and said, "Okay, I'm ready."

"Well, the story goes like this. Once there was a very rich man who built a wonderful mansion. He decorated it with the most expensive furniture and fixtures.

"For his large dining room, he ordered a magnificent chandelier which was to hang from the ceiling. Now, the chandelier was really something very special. It was made out of the most expensive crystal and rare glass ornaments.

"Now, when the chandelier arrived, the rich man was surprised to find out that it was so heavy, it couldn't hang from the ceiling. For if he would hang it up like that, it would surely come crashing down. So he ordered the workers to make a hole in the ceiling and to slide the chain right through the hole.

"Then he had the heavy chain tied very tightly and carefully to a strong post which was in the attic upstairs. Now he was sure that the gigantic chandelier would hang safely.

"After all was set and ready, the rich man invited all of his friends to come and marvel at the beautiful sight. It didn't take long, and the dining room was filled with the guests from all over who came to see this beautiful chandelier.

"In the midst of all the excitement, a beggar came knocking at the door asking for some food. The butler explained to the poor man that the owner is too busy now to see him in person as he did every time. He asked the beggar to go around to the back of the house where he would give him some food.

"After giving the poor man some food, the butler noticed the torn clothes that the beggar was wearing. He said to the beggar, 'We have some good used clothing in the attic. I think you could make some good use of them.'

"The beggar thanked him for the kind words and followed him to the stairway leading to the attic. The butler said to him, 'Go upstairs and help yourself.'

"Up in the attic, the poor man selected some of the used clothing that would fit him. As he was about to leave, he stopped to find a piece of rope with which to tie the bundle of clothing. He noticed a rope tied to the post in the attic. 'This is just what I need,' he thought to himself.

"Saying this, he took out a small knife and cut the rope. All of a sudden, there was a thunderous roar. The entire house shook at its very foundation. Alas, the large chandelier came crashing down.

"Now, you can imagine what took place in the dining room as the gigantic masterpiece came roaring down, right on top of the dining room table!

"The poor beggar failed to realize that by cutting the rope, he released the chain which was holding up the big chandelier.

"As the owner came rushing upstairs to the attic, he found the startled beggar standing right there before him, with a piece of rope in his hands.

"'Oh heavens!' the rich man called out. 'Look what you have done to me. I'm ruined!' The beggar looked at the rich man and pleaded, 'But please, all I did was cut this piece of rope, that's all!'

"Yes, dear Sarah," Father continued telling the story, "All he did was cut that piece of rope. But by doing this, he brought disaster to the rich man who was always so kind and generous to the beggar.

"You see, dear Sarah, there really is no such thing as a small sin. Yes, it may seem small to you, but one can never tell how awful it is in the eyes of Hashem."

Upon hearing this, Sarah looked up to her father and said, "Yes, you are so right. This story really teaches us such an important lesson. It teaches us not to listen to the Yetzer Hara who tries to trick us into doing an *Aveyrah*, a sin. We must always listen to the Yetzer Tov and do the lovely mitzvos of Hashem, G-d's holy commandments.

"Well, I must be on my way now. My friend is surely wondering why it's taking me so long to get to her house today, but I have some surprise for her. I'm going to tell her what happened to me today, and the lovely story you told me. I'm so sure that she'll enjoy it too!"

Father and Sarah wished each other a good Shabbos. Sarah went to her friend's house, and Father went to Shul to study Torah, in honor of the holy Shabbos.

The Big Barrel of Wine

Did you ever hear of the city called Grapetown? Well, the city of Grapetown is a very interesting city indeed. And there is a special reason why it's called Grapetown. For Grapetown was famous for the delicious wine that was made there. In fact, the people of that city were known as the merry wine-makers of Grapetown. And the wine they made was something special — it was so delicious!

People came from all parts of the country and from far away places just to get that delicious wine. As hard as they tried, the wine-makers of the other cities just couldn't make their wine taste so delicious as the wine made in Grapetown. Yes, Grapetown was a merry town, and so were all the people of Grapetown who earned their living by making the special delicious wine.

One day, something very strange happened, and Grapetown wasn't at all merry again. Something very sad happened, which brought about a big change in the city of Grapetown, and it all happened like this.

Early one morning, there was some excitement in the city. A large crowd gathered in the center of the marketplace. They were waiting for someone to arrive. They were waiting for the royal messenger who was to bring them an important message from his Majesty the King.

Finally, the large crowds cheered as the royal messenger arrived and took his place at the top of a platform which stood in the center of the marketplace. The crowd was hushed to a perfect silence as he unrolled a large scroll and began reading:

"Hear ye, hear ye! In ten days, his Majesty the King, is going to visit your city, the city of Grapetown. His Majesty has heard so much about the famous merry wine-makers of Grapetown and the delicious wine they produce, and therefore would like to honor them with a royal visit!"

Now, you can imagine how excited all the people of Grapetown became when they heard that the king himself is going to honor them with a royal visit!

Immediately they all gathered into the town hall to decide how to plan a grand welcome fitting for his Majesty the King!

Yes, once a year, the king would honor one of his cities with a royal visit and this year, it was Grapetown! Everyone offered some ideas and suggestions as how to make the grand welcome in a most impressive and honorable manner.

It didn't take long when they came up with a great idea. They all decided to build a very big barrel in the center of the marketplace. And this barrel was to be fifteen feet tall! And it was to be decorated in a most artistic manner, with colorful flowers and beautiful ornaments. And at the bottom of the gigantic barrel, there was to be a golden faucet.

Now can you guess what they were going to do with this gigantic barrel? Well, they were going to fill it up with the famous wine of Grapetown!

So every person living in Grapetown was ordered to bring one gallon of wine and pour it into the big barrel. By doing this, the entire barrel would be filled with the famous, delicious wine made by the merry wine-makers of Grapetown. And this is how they would greet the king. For when the king would arrive, they would lead him to this huge barrel of wine and honor him to be the first one to turn the golden faucet and fill his golden cup with the delicious wine of Grapetown.

Within moments, everyone left the town hall and got busy in preparing for the grand welcome! As soon as the gigantic barrel was built and artistically decorated from top to bottom, a long ladder was placed at the side of the barrel so that everyone could climb up to the top of the barrel and pour in one gallon of wine.

Now, everything seemed to be going along pretty well, until something very tragic happened.

In the city of Grapetown, there was a barber called Getzel, and he was so anxious to be the first one to get to the big barrel and pour in the first gallon of wine. But as he was about to fill his bottle with wine, he thought to himself, "My, this wine is so expensive. It would be foolish to give away so much precious wine. What would happen if I would pour water into the large barrel instead of wine? No one would be able to tell the difference. After all, with so many people in Grapetown, and each one pouring a full gallon of wine into the grape barrel, just one gallon of water wouldn't make a difference after all."

So Getzel the Barber filled his bottle with water and poured it into the big barrel.

Well, that wouldn't have been so tragic after all. That is, if it was only Getzel the Barber who poured water into the barrel.

But, alas, Beryl the Butcher, Chaim the Tailor, and Hershel the Shoemaker also came up with the same idea, and they also poured water into the barrel.

Oh, how awful. They were making such a foolish mistake! They thought, "Why should I bring wine? Let someone else do it!" not realizing that someone else may say the same thing.

And so, that's exactly what happened. Everyone in Grapetown was too selfish and too greedy to give away a gallon of wine, and they thought they could fool everyone else by bringing water. So everyone brought water and there wasn't a drop of wine in the big barrel.

My, were they in for a surprise, for the great day finally arrived and his Majesty the King, came to Grapetown.

The king was so pleased to see the beautifully decorated gigantic barrel built especially for him. The governor of the city was called upon to honor the king with a golden cup and direct the king to the golden faucet.

"Your Majesty," said the governor, "We have been honored with the king's visit and wish to show our true appreciation for such a majestic honor. And therefore we wish to present his Majesty with this golden cup. And as the king will turn the golden faucet, out will come the delicious wine, prepared by the merry wine-makers of Grapetown."

The crowd was hushed to a perfect silence as the king reached out and placed the golden cup under the golden faucet. Slowly, the king turned the faucet, and you can guess what happened! For instead of delicious wine, out came water!

Just plain water!

Oh, how embarrassing. Oh, how awful! Now the wine-makers of Grapetown had failed to gain favor in the eyes of his Majesty the King.

How will they ever be explain to the king what had happened? Who knows how long they will have to wait until they will again be worthy of having the king honor them with a royal visit.

Yes, this story teaches us an important lesson to remember at all times. If there is something good to do, do it yourself. Never say, "Let someone else do it," for someone else may say the same thing, and it will never be done.

As the Torah teaches us, always set yourself as a good example in doing what is good in the eyes of Hashem so that others may follow you and do the same.

THE LITTLE AVROHOM

The Little Avraham

It was a bright, sunny day and Little Avraham walked along the soft sands of the seashore. He was looking for something and he found it. He was just three years old when it all happened.

Here he was, walking along slowly by the seashore. Every now and then, he would stop, pick up a shell or a stone, examine it carefully, and then put it down.

Little Avraham marveled at the wonders of nature, the gigantic roaring seas, the curling waves, lofty mountains, tall trees, the flowers, and the birds. In fact, he marveled at everything he set his eyes upon for everything meant something to him.

Suddenly he stopped, looked up, and said to himself, "Where did this beautiful world come from? Who made this wonderful world?"

That's when the search began. Little Avraham was set on finding the answer to the question, Who created the heavens and earth?

At first, he looked up to the blue sky and saw the blazing sun, shining so brightly from above, bringing light and warmth everywhere.

"Could this be the Creator of heavens and earth?" he thought. "Could this be G-d?"

But as he noticed how the bright sun kept moving slowly across the sky and finally disappeared out of sight, he said to himself, "No, this can't be G-d. Anything that comes for just a while and then goes away can't be G-d at all. G-d has to be present at all times."

And so, Little Avraham kept on searching for the G-d who is eternal and forever.

It didn't take long, and suddenly, there appeared from above the bright and radiant moon. Oh how magnificent! Its soft rays reaching out and melting away the darkness that blanketed the earth!

"Could this be G-d? Could this be the Creator of heavens and earth?" But again, Little Avraham noticed how the moon moved slowly across the face of the sky and then finally disappeared out of sight.

"No, no," he said. "This can't be G-d at all. G-d is forever. G-d is present at all times. I must find G-d. I will not give up until I find the true G-d, the real G-d, the Creator of heavens and earth."

At that moment, Little Avraham noticed how the entire heavens became filled with a countless number of sparking and twinkling stars.

"Oh how majestic!" he called out. "Oh how beautiful! Is it possible that there are many, many gods?" he thought for a moment.

But again he noticed how they too soon disappeared from sight. Little Avraham realized that he must continue to search until he finds G-d, for he was sure that G-d was not the sun, the moon, nor the stars. He stood motionless, deep in thought, asking himself, "Who is G-d? And where can I find Him?"

Then, suddenly, the answer came to him. "There is only one G-d, the one and only creator of heavens and earth. He created the sun, the moon, and the stars. He created everything. He cannot be seen, but he is everywhere at all times."

Little Avraham leapt for joy, for he finally found what he was looking for.

"I must go now and tell this to everyone. I want everyone to know about the G-d that I have found."

Well, it is no surprise at all to know that this Little Avraham grew up to be the very first Jew. We know him as Avraham Aveinu, Abraham our Father, the first Jew who taught the entire world about the one and only G-d.

And we, his children, proudly proclaim, "*Shema Yisroel, Hashem Elokainu, Hashem Echad.* Hear O Israel, Hashem is our G-d, Hashem is One."

The Three Sacks of Gold

There once was a king who selected three great artists to decorate one of the rooms of his royal palace. Each of the artists was to decorate one of the walls of the room. To pay them for their work, he set aside three sacks filled with gold, one larger than the other.

The largest sack of gold was to be given to the artist who will make the nicest painting. The smaller sack of gold was to be given to the artist who will make the second best painting. And the smallest sack of gold was to be given to the third artist.

The king told them to have the work completed within thirty days. The three artists were so thrilled with the work given to them that they immediately returned home to prepare the supplies for their work.

Early the next morning, one of the artists arrived at the royal palace. He brought along all his supplies and immediately got to work. He began drawing a picture on one of the three walls.

He realized that all he had were thirty days during which he was to complete his masterpiece of artwork. So, each day he would arrive early in the morning and work until late in the night.

Seven days had already passed and there was no sign of the other two artists. During this time, the first artist had already made fine progress in his drawings.

Finally, the second artist arrived. He immediately got to work on his wall, realizing that he had only twenty three days left in which he was to complete his artwork for the king.

Twenty days had already passed and there were only ten days left to finish the artwork. Strangely enough, there still was no sign of the third artist. For while the two artists were so busy drawing their masterpiece on their wall, the third wall remained empty. Everyone wondered, "Where can he be? Why is it taking him so long to get to the royal palace?"

Twenty eight days passed and the two artists had already completed their masterpiece of artwork. For the remaining two days, they kept on adding the delicate and fine finishing touches to their painting so that it find favor in the eyes of the king.

Of course, as much as the second artist tried to make his painting presentable, nevertheless, it wasn't as beautiful as the painting of the first artist who spent so much more time on his drawing. It was quite clear by now that the first artist was entitled to the largest sack of gold, while the second artist would be awarded the smaller sack of gold. But alas, what about the third artist? Where is he?

Oh my — another day had already passed and still no sign or trace of him. And look at his wall! It's still empty. How is he ever going to finish his work on time?

There was much excitement at the royal palace as the thirtieth day finally arrived.

The king had invited all of the members of the royal palace to come and witness the presentation of the rewards and to marvel at the beauty of the fine masterpieces.

To top it off, the air was filled with suspense and excitement, for everyone was trying to figure out the answer to the mystery of the third artist. He seemed to have disappeared into thin air.

Well, I'm going to let you in on a secret. For while the two artists were working so hard to win first prize, the third artist was taking it easy. He wasn't working at all. For he had planned a trick — a trick through which he thought he would win the first prize.

Now can you guess what he had in mind? Well, let's continue with the story and you'll find out.

"Oh my, look ahead!" called out one of the guards of the royal palace.

"Look at that wagon coming towards the royal gate! And what's that large thing on top of the wagon? Why, it's covered with a white cloth. And look who's leading the way! Why, it's the third artist!"

Everyone cheered as the third artist passed the royal gate and led the strange looking wagon to the steps of the palace.

Yes, it was the thirtieth day and the third artist finally arrived. Everyone was wondering what was that strange looking thing that the servants were taking off the wagon and carrying towards the room where the two artists were standing.

You can imagine how surprised the two artists were when they saw the third artist finally arrive. "Oh my!" they called out. "While we were working on our artwork here in the royal palace, you were drawing your masterpiece at home and now you brought it here."

The third artist said nothing but kept himself busy, showing the servants where to hang up his master-piece. "Do not remove the sheet from my masterpiece," he ordered. "I will do this myself at the right time."

The long-awaited for moment finally arrived and the trumpets were sounded to announce the arrival of the king.

All the guests were hushed to a perfect silence as the king entered into the newly decorated room. Following the king were three servants, each one holding a sack of gold, one larger than the other.

Carefully, the king examined the fine paintings on the two walls. His face was radiant as he smiled so joyfully, admiring the fine masterpieces of artwork.

As he came close to the third wall, the third artist stepped forward and said, "Your Majesty, here is my masterpiece." Saying this, he removed the white sheet from the wall and, alas, there it was — a fine masterpiece indeed!

The other two artists couldn't believe their eyes. For on the third wall was the reflection of both of their paintings.

Yes, this was the trick the third artist had planned, for all that he brought to the royal palace was a large glass mirror.

Everyone in the room held their breath in surprise as they stood motionlessly, wondering how the king would distribute the sacks of gold. Would it be fair to give the first prize to the third artist since both of the other paintings are reflected on his wall?

Well, the king realized what was happening.

"How awful," he thought to himself, "This artist wishes to be rewarded for the work of the other artists. I must teach him a lesson. He must learn that one can be rewarded only for the work he does himself and never claim reward for the work of others."

The king stepped forward and called for the servant holding the largest sack of gold.

"Hang up this sack of gold next to the picture of the first artist," he said. Then he ordered the servant holding the smaller sack of gold to hang it up next to the picture of the second artist.

The air was again filled with suspense, as everyone wondered what will the king do next.

At this moment, the king walked over to the third artist and said, "Congratulations for your fine piece of work. For such a fine masterpiece, you deserve not one, but two, sacks of gold."

Everyone in the room was shocked to hear this, especially the two artists who worked so hard for their reward.

Upon hearing this, the third artist leaped for joy. "Oh thank you, your Majesty! Thank you very much! Now, can I please have the two sacks of gold?"

"What do you mean?" asked the king. "Why, they are hanging on your wall! Don't you see them? Right next to the pictures."

And pointing to the mirror, the king said to the third artist, "Go over and take them."

And, of course, this would be impossible for it was only the reflection of the other two walls.

Yes, this story has an important lesson for all of us. As our Chachamim, our wise men, tell us "*Yogatee u'Motzosee*," only if you work hard, will you find it.

Never expect to be rewarded for doing nothing. Put all of your efforts into your work, then you will be entitled to enjoy the good reward that follows.

For when Hashem sees you doing your best, He will surely bless you with true success and good reward.

The Return of Little Tzip Tzip

Tzip Tzip is a birdy. Not just a birdy, but a very, very little birdy just about ready to stretch out its little soft wings and begin to fly for the very first time.

Tzip Tzip's mommy said to her, "Oh my! Look at your wings! They seem to be strong enough. How about taking your first trip out of the nest?"

At first, little Tzip Tzip was a bit frightened. She was worried, for this would be the very first time that Tzip Tzip would go away from the nest. Until now, she was so close to her mommy; they were always together in the comfortable and warm nest.

Well, Tzippy finally took mommy's advice and began to stretch out her soft wings and began, for the first time, to skip around in the nest.

"Look, Mommy!" Tzip Tzip called. "Look! I'm hopping all around. Gee, this is fun!"

"Well, Tzip Tzip, now you are ready to take a trip far away from the nest."

Little Tzip Tzip was so excited. She practiced this new and exciting adventure every day. She would fly back and forth, each time flying a bit further until she said to her mother, "Mommy, now that I can fly for quite a far distance, where should I go?"

To this, Mother answered, "Very well, very well. You may fly in any direction. You may fly to the North or to the South. You may even fly to the East or to the West. In fact, you may fly anywhere. Go right ahead, Tzip Tzip. Go out and discover a new world, a world that is filled with so many things that are so good. That is, only if you really search for them. If you will look for the good things in this lovely world, you will surely find them."

And off she flew, waving goodbye to Mommy as she began her first long trip, away from her nest, away from Mommy.

Tzip Tzip headed towards the East. She wanted to know what was doing in the East. And off she went on this very exciting adventure. But as soon as she got to the East, she waited for a moment, looked around, and turned back home. That's right! Back to the nest, back to Mommy.

"What's the matter?" asked Mother. "What's the matter, little Tzip Tzip? Why have you returned so quickly? Don't you like the East?"

Little Tzip Tzip looked up and said, "Oh Mommy, I don't know how to tell this to you, but it smells so bad in the East. I just can't stand it!"

Upon hearing this, Mother said, "Very well, Tzip Tzip, very well. Then why don't you try going to the West. Perhaps you will like it there."

And off went Tzip Tzip to explore the West for the very first time.

But as soon as Tzip Tzip arrived in the West she looked around and took one deep sniff...and said to herself, "Uh-uh. I can't stay here at all. My, there's such a strange smell in the West. I must return back home. I'm going back to Mommy."

And so, again, little Tzip Tzip turned around and headed back home to her nest, to Mommy.

Well, I'm sure you can guess what happened next. That's right, Mother sent Tzip Tzip to the North only for Tzip Tzip to return, and the very same happened when she sent her to the South.

Upon seeing this, Mother said to Tzip Tzip, "Come over here please. Let me take a good look at you." As Mother looked at Tzip Tzip, she began to laugh, "Ha-ha. Oh look what I found!"

Tzip Tzip looked up. "Mother, please tell me what did you find?"

"Well, I want you to know that on the tip of your nose was a piece of dirt that you didn't even notice. You see, Tzip Tzip, there's no bad smell in the North or in the South. Not in the East or in the West. It was this piece of dirt that you were smelling. So wherever you would go, you would have that strange smell."

Well, quickly Mother wiped the nose of Tzip Tzip until it was absolutely clean again. She said to her, "Tzip Tzip, now you can fly anywhere and you don't have to worry about those strange smells anymore."

Yes, the mystery of the strange smells was finally solved, and I want you to know there's a wonderful lesson that we can learn from this story, a lesson that could teach us something so very important.

You see, in the Torah, Hashem commands us to love one another, as it is written, *"V'ohavta L'rai-acha Ko-mocho.* You are to love your fellowman just as much as you love yourself."

Now, this can be possible only if we will look at our fellowman with a good eye. It means to take notice of your friend's good qualities. By doing this, you will surely admire your friend's good qualities and try to follow them too.

In fact, this is the way to be able to practice the lovely mitzvah of *Ahavas Yisroel,* to love one another.

And the great famous rabbi, Reb Yisroel Baal Shem Tov said, in case we ever notice any faults in our fellowman, we should imagine as if we are looking into a mirror. That's right, for as we look in a mirror we see the image of ourself.

So, the fault that you see in your friend, may truly be a fault of your own.

And our *Chachamim*, our wise men, teach us in the Talmud, *K'shot Atzmecho T'chila*, first correct your own faults, *V'achar Kach K'shot Achay-rim*, and then you may correct the faults of others. For as you correct yourself, your fellow man will accept you as a living example. He will admire you and try to do the same.

Yes, just like in the story of little Tzip Tzip, the fault that she found everywhere else was truly her own, and Tzip Tzip's mommy taught her a lovely rule. Correct your own faults first, and then you will find yourself in a much nicer and better world in which to live — a world filled with love and true peace.

Let's Say
Baruch Hashem

"Shalom dear children, how are you today?"

"Baruch Hashem fine. And how are you today?"

"Oh, Baruch Hashem fine. Thank you!"

"You're welcome."

There once lived a very great rabbi by the name of Reb Yisroel Baal Shem Tov. He was very famous for all the wonderful things he did. There were so many students who would come to him to learn Hashem's holy Torah. With loving care, he taught them how to serve Hashem with true joy and happiness.

One of the most important things he taught them was to remember that Hashem is always watching over us. He is protecting us and blessing us with all good.

The Baal Shem Tov also explained to his students how much Hashem enjoys listening to us bless Him. And in return, Hashem blesses us with long life, good health, and true happiness.

This is why Reb Yisroel would so often visit the marketplace where he would meet many people. He would go over to them and ask, "How are you today?" Only to hear them say, *"Baruch Hashem,* fine!"

That's right, Reb Yisroel wanted to hear them say *Baruch Hashem,* for he knew how much Hashem enjoys it and blesses them too.

So, let's learn these two words and use them as often as we can. For each time we call out *"Baruch Hashem,"* we are reminding ourselves of Hashem and we are blessing Him too.

Oh what a lovely thing to do! It makes Hashem so happy! And for this, He will bless you too.

And to remember this lovely rule, let's learn a new song. It will remind you to always bless Hashem and to thank Him for all the good things He does for you.

And here are the words to the song:

Baruch Hashem, Baruch Hashem,
Is what I always say.
To show my thanks to Hashem,
Every single day.
Baruch Hashem, Baruch Hashem,
Praise Hashem forever,
And bless His holy name.
Baruch Hashem, Baruch Hashem,
Let's join in together and say it once again.

THE HOUR OF FORTUNE

The Hour of Fortune

This story is about a king and his faithful servant called Yisroel. The king had many servants in the royal palace. They served him faithfully, with devotion and dedication. Yet Yisroel was different. His service was really outstanding. Of all the servants in the royal palace, the king favored Yisroel. His genuine devotion and sincere dedication was unequaled by any of the other servants.

There was something in the way he served his Majesty the King. He did all in his power to please the king and to bring him delight and contentment. No wonder why the king favored him more than all the other servants in the royal palace.

Years passed and it came the time for Yisroel to be promoted to a higher position in the royal palace. As it was the custom in the royal kingdom, however, before any servant was to be promoted to a higher position, he would be given a test by his Majesty the King himself. Through this test, the king would determine which position would be best for him.

So, Yisroel was called to appear before his Majesty the King. The king said to him, "Yisroel, you have been in my royal palace for many years. During this time, you have had the opportunity to enter into almost all of the rooms of my royal palace, that is, all except one, my own secret room of treasures — the room where I have stored away a fortune of diamonds, gold, silver, jewels, priceless gems, and countless treasures. Now, in appreciation for the many years of your faithful service, I am going to let you go into my room of treasures and permit you to take for yourself anything you wish."

Well, you can imagine how surprised Yisroel was when the king told him the good news. He just couldn't believe what he was hearing. He just stood there speechless.

"I must be dreaming," he thought to himself. "Can this really be true?" he wondered.

Upon noticing the surprised look on Yisroel's face, the king said, "Yisroel, I want you to know there is one condition, however, that is, you may remain in the royal room of treasures for just one hour, and as soon as the hour is up, you must leave the room immediately.

"But during this hour, you may take for yourself anything you wish. And it will be yours for keeps! So Yisroel, tomorrow morning at nine o'clock I will lead you through the golden gates of the royal room of treasures. These gates will remain open for one full hour."

The king wished Yisroel good luck and bid him farewell. Yisroel left the king's room and immediately went down to the storage room of the royal palace to select for himself ten large barrels. He planned to fill the barrels with all the royal treasures he can possibly gather during the hour of fortune.

It was early the next morning and Yisroel was busy bringing the ten large barrels into the hall that lead to the treasury room. You can imagine how excited he was. He just couldn't wait for the stroke of nine when he would be able to enter into the royal room of treasures.

Alas! His Majesty the king finally arrived and signaled Yisroel to follow him towards the golden gates. Quickly, Yisroel lined up the ten large barrels, right before the golden gates. He wanted to enter into the room at the stroke of nine. He realized how precious every second was during the hour of fortune.

Finally, the hour of fortune approached. The two golden gates swung open and the king turned to Yisroel saying, "Enter, my dear servant. Enter into my room of treasures. And take for yourself anything you wish."

"Oh thank you, your Majesty," said Yisroel, as he passed through the two golden gates and headed for a large heap of sparkling diamonds piled up on the floor of the room.

He reached out with both hands and was just about ready to dig his fingers into the pile of diamonds when all of a sudden something very strange happened, something very strange indeed.

For some mysterious reason, he remained standing completely motionless. He just stood there, gazing at the sparkling diamonds, without making any move at all.

What happened? Why isn't he taking any of the diamonds?

Well, as you remember, the king was only testing Yisroel. He wanted to find out how smart he really was, and this is what he did.

The king knew that Yisroel loved to listen to music. He enjoyed music more than anything else. So the king appointed one of the finest musicians to come along with him into the room of treasures and ordered him to play the finest pieces of music for one full hour. And this was the test. The king wanted to see what choice Yisroel would make. Would he spend every precious moment gathering up the royal treasures for himself? Or would he waste these precious moments just listening to music?

The large clock on the wall kept ticking away the precious moments, and there stood his Majesty the King by the golden gates, watching Yisroel very closely. And strangely enough, Yisroel was just standing there motionless. He noticed the violinist in the corner of the room, playing the finest music he had ever heard before.

Yisroel thought to himself, "Oh what lovely music. I must listen to this. I will spend just a few minutes listening to such fine music. And for the rest of the hour, I will gather these treasures for myself."

Well, it just didn't happen that way, for just as a few minutes passed and the violinist noticed Yisroel heading for the pile of diamonds, he began to play another piece of music. It was even more enchanting and finer than the music he played before.

Instead of gathering the royal treasures, Yisroel was again just listening to the fine music. Little did he realize, that by gathering the royal treasures now, he would be so fortunate and so wealthy, he would have more than enough money to hire the best musician to play for him for the rest of his life.

And so, this is what happened, each time Yisroel decided to begin gathering the royal treasures, the violinist would begin to play a different masterpiece, until the final moments of the hour of fortune approached.

And there stood his Majesty the King, next to the ten large empty barrels. The king pointed to the large clock on the wall as the hour of fortune finally came to an end.

After a few moments of silence, the king called to Yisroel and said, "Come, my dear servant, come. The hour of fortune is over and you must leave now."

Yisroel called out, "But your Majesty, please, let me take just one handful of these precious diamonds."

"I'm sorry, Yisroel," said the king. "You had a whole hour in which to gather these treasures and now that the hour is up you must leave."

Yisroel sadly bowed his head before the king, as he walked by the ten large empty barrels and left the royal room of treasures empty-handed.

Well, I would like you to know that there is something special about this story. That is, this is not just another story that happened long, long ago. In fact, it's happening right now, and you are in this story!

For the king in this story is Hashem, the King of all kings, the Creator of the heavens and earth. And the servant in this story, why that's you! And the royal room of treasures, that is right here on this lovely world we live in. You see, Hashem places us on this world to live for a certain amount of time, and during this time we have to gather all of the wonderful treasures that He placed here.

Hashem also showed us where to find these precious treasures. This is why Hashem gave us His holy Torah. For the Torah teaches us how and where to find these lovely treasures. And, of course, these treasures are the lovely mitzvos, the commandments we learn in Hashem's holy Torah. Oh yes, that's right!

Every time we do a mitzvah, that is, we are respectful to our parents, we give Tzedakah (charity), we recite a *Bracha*, a blessing, we light the Shabbos candles, put on Tefillin, and so many, many more lovely mitzvos. By doing this, we are gathering for ourselves endless fortunes and treasures to enjoy both on this world and in the World to Come.

But as you remember in the story, the king ordered a musician to play lovely music only to attract the attention of Yisroel, and to see what choice he would make. The same is with us, the musician in our own story is the *Yetzer Hara* that Hashem puts into us only to see what we will choose. That's right, that's the little voice in us that tries to attract our attention and keep us back from learning Hashem's Torah and from doing any mitzvos.

So, let us remember this story, and whenever the Yetzer Hara tries to keep us from doing anything that's good, or tempts us to do anything that is wrong, let's not pay any attention to him at all. Instead, let's learn more and more Torah, and do as many mitzvos as we possibly can. And for this, Hashem will surely bless us all with a long life in good health and true happiness for all of us to enjoy, both on this world and in the World to Come.

The Mystery of the Overturned Inkwell

"In the beginning, Hashem created the heavens and the earth."

These are the words with which Hashem begins his holy Torah. At the very beginning of the Torah, we learn that Hashem created the heavens and earth and all of their creatures, that he is the Master and Ruler of the whole world. He created it, He keeps it alive, and controls it.

A rabbi was once called to appear before a king. The king would often invite the wise men of his country to the royal palace. He would spend many hours with them as they shared words of wisdom with one another.

Many times, the king would ask the wise men questions they could not answer, and this is when he would call for the rabbi. The king admired the rabbi for his wisdom, for he knew that the rabbi was forever learning Torah through which he became so intelligent and wise. The king was delighted from the way the rabbi would answer these difficult questions so brilliantly.

The rabbi was led to the room where his Majesty the King was anxiously awaiting his arrival. After sharing greetings with one another, the king said to the rabbi, "I know you are a man of great wisdom. You learn the Torah. I have a question to ask you. I have asked this question to many of the wise men of the royal palace and they could find no answer to it. Perhaps you can help me."

"Your Majesty," said the rabbi, "I shall try my best."

"My question is, where did this great world come from?"

"Why, your Majesty," said the rabbi, "Our Torah answers that question right at the very first sentence. 'In the beginning, G-d created the heavens and the earth.'"

"Very well, dear rabbi," said the king. "But can you give me some good explanation so I may understand this more clearly? Why can't we say that this world just happened to be here by itself? For what good reason must we say that it was all created by G-d?"

There was a moment of silence in the room as the rabbi remained in deep thought preparing the answer to the king's question, when all of a sudden something very strange happened. For there was a large inkwell on the king's desk and accidentally, the king rubbed his elbow against the inkwell and it turned on its side, spilling out the ink all over the desk.

"Oh my," said the king, "look what I have done. I'm going to call for one of my servants to clean this up."

Saying this, the king stood up and left the room. As the king left the room, the rabbi thought of a wise thing to do.

Quickly, he took some paper and carefully wiped off all of the ink from the desk. Then he took another clean sheet of paper and began to draw a picture on it. Being a fine artist, the rabbi made a picture of the beautiful scenery that can be seen through the window of the king's room — the blue sky, the brilliant sun, the lofty mountains covered with tall trees and green grass, a flowing river, surrounded by an orchard of colorful flowers.

As he finished the fine drawing, he put it on the king's desk, and right next to it, he placed the overturned inkwell.

As the king returned with the servant, he was surprised to find the masterpiece of fine art on his desk. He called out in surprise, "Oh rabbi! Who made this fine masterpiece and where did this come from?"

"Why, your Majesty," answered the rabbi, "don't you remember? This inkwell turned over, and as the ink rolled over the paper, it formed this lovely picture."

"Oh Rabbi," said the king, "how can you say such a thing. Why that's just impossible! Why this fine drawing must have been made by a great artist. Why look at the fine work put into this picture. Are you trying to tell me that all of this happened by itself? Why nothing can happen by itself."

"Yes, your Majesty. You are so right. Nothing can happen by itself!"

Upon saying this, the rabbi pointed towards the tall window and said to the king, "Please, your Majesty, look here. See this beautiful world, the blazing sun from above, the blue sky, and the lofty mountains. Look at the tall trees and beautiful flowers, the flowing river and colorful orchards. Can we think for a moment that this all happened by itself? Surely, this is the work of a great artist! A great master, that is, Hashem, the Creator of heavens and earth.

"True, it was I who made this picture, only to prove to you that there surely is a great Master who created this wonderful world."

Upon hearing this, the king raised his hands and said, "Blessed be Hashem, the Creator of heavens and earth. And blessed be the children of Israel, who study Hashem's holy Torah and follow its teachings."

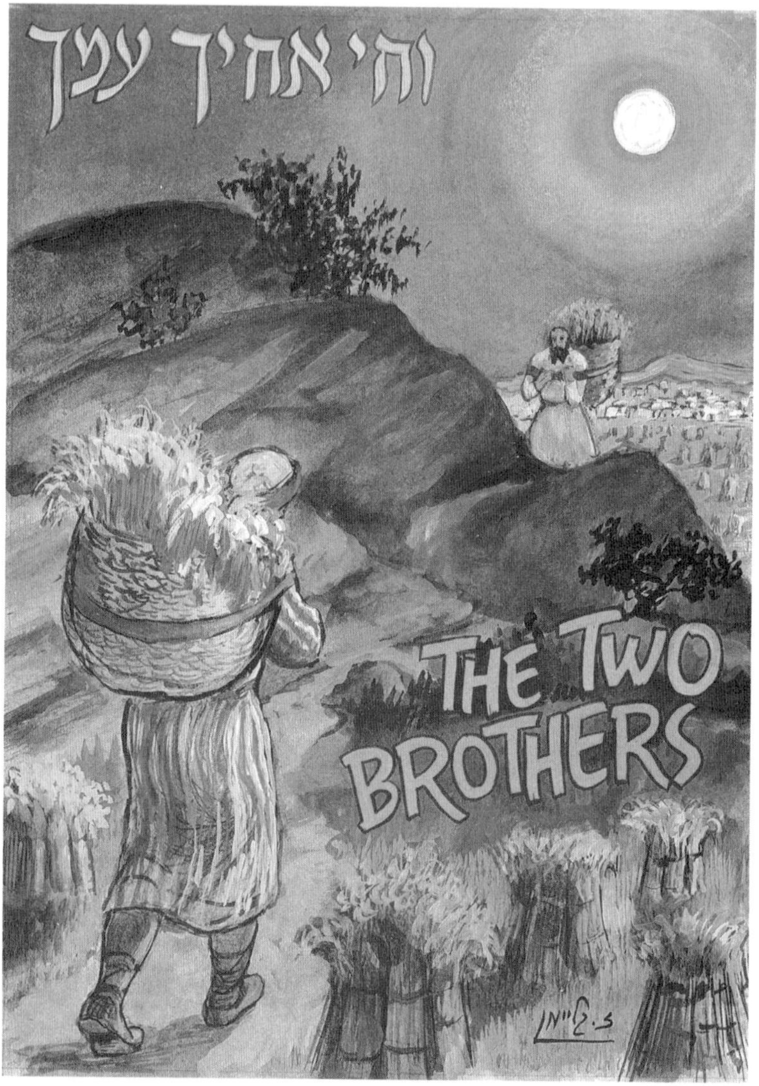
וחי אחיך עמך
THE TWO BROTHERS

The Two Brothers

Of all the lands in the world, Hashem selected Eretz Yisroel, the land of Israel, to be His land. Of all the cities in Eretz Yisroel, Hashem selected Yerushalayim, Jerusalem, to be His holy city. Of all the mountains in Yerushalayim, Hashem selected Har HaMoriah, Mount Moriah, upon which to build His *Beis HaMikdash*, the holy temple.

On this *Har HaKodesh*, this holy mountain, stood the first and second Beis HaMikdash. And on this very same place, Hashem will rebuild the third Beis HaMikdash, very soon, speedily in our days, through the arrival of *Moshiach Tzidkeinu*, our Righteous Redeemer, who will gather us all from the four corners of the world and return us all to our holy land, Eretz Yisroel.

There are many reasons why Hashem selected Har HaMoriah to be the mountain upon which to build His Beis HaMikdash. The Torah tells us that our Father Abraham, Avraham Aveinu, built a *Mizbayach*, an altar, on that mountain, upon which he was ready to sacrifice his beloved son, Yitzchok, as commanded by Hashem Himself.

Yes, this mountain is really something special, for it is a symbol of sacrifice and devotion. It is also a symbol of true love and brotherhood.

Our Chachamim, our wise men, tell us of a strange and interesting story that happened on this mountain many, many years ago.

There once lived two brothers. One was called Reuven, and the other, Shimon. Reuven was blessed with many children, but Shimon had none. They were both farmers. Each one had a large field of his own. They both worked very hard on their fields from which they earned a living.

The time of harvest came, and both Reuven and Shimon were busy in the field, cutting the wheat. As Shimon stood in his field, a thought came to him, "My brother Reuven has such a large family to support. He must need much more money than I do. I must help him. I'm going to take a large amount of my wheat and place it in his field, and he will not know where it came from. But I will have to do this when he is not around. I don't want him to know that it was I who brought the wheat into his field."

So, Shimon decided to wait until midnight, for he was sure that Reuven would be fast asleep at that time. Shimon tied together many large bundles of wheat and set them aside to bring to Reuven's field that night.

Now, that very same day, Reuven was also in the field and a thought came to him, "Oh, my brother, Shimon, is so unfortunate. He has no children at all. There's no one to help him with the work on the farm. He has to do it all alone. He can just barely manage to get enough wheat to support himself. I must do something to help him."

So, Reuven decided to set aside a large amount of wheat, which he was going to bring over to his brother's field.

"My brother must not know that it was I who brought this wheat to him," thought Reuven. "This may embarrass him." So he decided to wait until midnight when he was sure that Shimon would be fast asleep.

Well, little did they know that they were in for some surprise, for as midnight approached, Reuven gathered together the large bundles of wheat and headed towards Shimon's field. Now Shimon, too, did exactly the same. He tied together all the wheat and began to carry it to Reuven's field.

Now, the two fields were separated by a mountain, and there was a road which surrounded the mountain. Reuven and Shimon would usually use this road in order to get to each other's field. However, this time, Reuven thought it would not be wise to use the regular road for he didn't want to be noticed by anyone. So he decided to get to Shimon's field by climbing over the mountain.

And so, the same idea came to Shimon. He too wanted to get to his brother's field without being noticed, so he decided to climb over the mountain instead of using the road which surrounded it. And here we find Reuven and Shimon, each loaded with a large bundle of wheat, climbing the mountain at the very same time. And at any moment, both of them will reach the very top of the mountain.

Oh my, are they in for a surprise! Can you imagine what is going to happen when they both meet each other, face to face, at the top of the mountain?

The moon was shining very brightly, as Reuven and Shimon finally reached the very top of the mountain. They began heading towards the other side. And this is when it all happened.

For all of a sudden Reuven noticed from the distance someone walking towards him. "Who can that be?" he thought to himself.

Shimon too was amazed to notice someone coming towards him. As they kept coming closer, they finally recognized each other. There they stood, motionless.

It was at this point where they both realized what was happening. They remained standing silently.

There they stood with the heavy load of wheat on their shoulders. They were both puzzled. They just didn't know what to do.

Suddenly, each one threw down his load of wheat and ran towards his brother. They hugged and kissed each other, and with tears of joy in their eyes, they began to dance and laugh.

Yes, they realized that they both planned to do the very same thing. The ever-watchful eye of Hashem saw this strange meeting, how two brothers showed true love to each other and how each one was so strongly concerned in helping his brother. This brought about so much delight and contentment to Hashem that He called out in joy, "I can find no better place upon which to build My Beis HaMikdash than on this very spot where two brothers have shown such true love and devotion to one another."

Yes, this story took place many, many years ago, right on the top of Har HaMoriah in the holy city of Yerushalayim. Let's remember this story; it has an important lesson for all of us. It teaches us to love each other. It reminds us that Hashem is our Father and we are His children. And this is why we are to consider each other as our own sister and brother. Let's show this true love by sharing our blessings with one another.

Let's give Tzedakah, charity. Let's help our sisters and brothers through teaching them Hashem's holy Torah and lovely commandments.

This will certainly bring joy and delight to Hashem for which He will surely bless us all and reward us with a *"Geulah Sh'laymo V'amitis,"* a complete and true redemption, through sending us Moshiach, our true Redeemer, who will free us all from this final *Golus*, exile, and return us all to our holy land, Eretz Yisroel, where Hashem will rebuild His third Beis HaMikdash, on this holy mountain Har HaMoriah, speedily, in our days. Amen!

HERE COMES REB YO- SEF HU- RAY HU- RAY

REB YOSEF MOKIR SHABBOS

שבת קי"ט א'

Reb Yosef Mokir Shabbos

Of all the days of the week, Hashem blessed the day of Shabbos and made it holy. The day of Shabbos is a day of rest, for in six days, Hashem created the whole world, the heavens and earth and all of their creatures, and on the seventh day, the day of Shabbos, Hashem rested from all of His work.

Here is a story about a very kind-hearted person. His name was Reb Yosef.

He was known to all as Reb Yosef Mokir Shabbos. Mokir Shabbos means 'one who honors the Shabbos'. He was given this name because of the lovely way he used to honor the day of Shabbos.

Every Thursday morning, Reb Yosef would get up extra early and go to the fish market. There he would select the largest fish to take home *L'Kovod Shabbos Kodesh*, in honor of the holy Shabbos. At home, Reb Yosef's wife would prepare the most delicious gefilte fish in town.

Every Friday afternoon, Reb Yosef would invite all the poor people of his town to come to his house. There he would give them a large dish of gefilte fish to take home for the day of Shabbos.

Yes, Reb Yosef was such a kind person, he wanted to have all the poor people of his town join him in the lovely mitzvah of eating delicious gefilte fish in honor of the holy day of Shabbos. And it was some sight to watch Reb Yosef return from the fish market with a big, big fish on his shoulders. Everyone in town would come out to greet him on the way.

Oh, Reb Yosef's face would shine from joy as he would come marching down the street, showing everyone the big, big fish that he's bringing home for the Shabbos Tish, the Shabbos table.

Now, as the people would crowd along the sides of the street to welcome Reb Yosef with the big, big fish, they would all burst out with a loud cheer and then sing a special welcoming song for Reb Yosef Mokir Shabbos.

And this is what they would sing to him:

Here comes Reb Yosef, hurray, hurray, with a big big fish for the Shabbos Tish, oh he's so kind I'll say. Hey! Here comes Reb Yosef, hurray, hurray, with a big, big fish for the Shabbos Tish, to honor the special day. With a big, big fish for the Shabbos Tish, to honor the special day.

And in return, this is what Reb Yosef would sing to them:

I'll treat you to a mitzvah today, today, with a big, big dish of Gefilte fish, please join me on the way. Hey, I'll treat you to a mitzvah, today, today, with a big, big dish of Gefilte fish L'Kovod the Shabbos day. With a big, big dish of Gefilte fish L'Kovod the Shabbos day.

Now, in the same town where Reb Yosef lived, there was a very rich man. He was called Yivan. Yivan was the richest person in town. But strangely enough, no one had anything to do with him, for he was a very selfish person. Never would he offer any help to the poor people of his town.

All the beggars knew that Yivan wouldn't even give a penny for Tzedakah, charity. They all felt sorry for Yivan. They pitied him, for he did not realize how lovely it is to be kind and to share your own fortune with others who are in need of help.

No wonder why Reb Yosef Mokir Shabbos was so loved and admired by all the people of his town, for he was such a kind person, whereas Yivan had no friends at all. He was all alone, for no one wishes to be friends with a person who is selfish.

One day, something very strange happened. It was late in the evening when suddenly, Yivan heard a knocking at the door.

"Who's there?" he called out.

"It is I, Kaldai the Stargazer. Please let me in. I have something very important to tell you."

Kaldai the Stargazer entered into the room and said to Yivan, "Yivan, I must tell you what I have seen in the stars tonight. They tell me that all of your treasures, gold and silver, and your entire belonging, will be taken away from you and will be given to Reb Yosef Mokir Shabbos."

Upon hearing this Yivan cried out, "Oh no! I must do something very quickly. This can't happen to me."

So Yivan went and sold all of his belongings, his treasures, gold and silver, and with the money, he bought a very large diamond. He took the diamond and sewed it into his hat.

"I will wear this hat wherever I go, and no one will ever know where I hid my fortune. Surely, no one can take it away from me now," Yivan said.

A few days later, Yivan went traveling on a ferry boat. All of a sudden, a very strong wind came along and blew off his hat.

"My hat! My hat!" he called.

Alas, his hat fell into the ocean.

Upon hearing Yivan's cry for help, one of the sailors dived into the water to get his hat. It didn't take long and the sailor came up with Yivan's hat in his hands.

Quickly, Yivan took the hat and began to examine it carefully. Suddenly, he called out loud, "Oh no! It's gone! It's gone!"

Yes, he discovered that the diamond was missing. It had fallen to the bottom of the ocean.

Poor Yivan returned home penniless. He was now just like the other poor beggars in town. It was now that he first began to realize how wrong it was to be selfish, and he was surely thankful that there were kind-hearted people in town who were ready to help him in his time of need.

It was Friday afternoon and Reb Yosef and his wife were busy getting ready for Shabbos. All of a sudden, a large wagon pulled over in front of their house. And the driver called out, "Reb Yosef! Reb Yosef! Look what I have for you!"

Reb Yosef looked out of the window and just couldn't believe his eyes. For on the wagon was the largest fish he had ever seen before.

"We just caught this big, big fish, and if you want it, you may have it for thirteen golden coins."

Quickly, Reb Yosef took out thirteen golden coins and paid the fisherman for the big, big fish. Reb Yosef and his wife called out in joy, "*Baruch Hashem*, blessed is G-d! Now we can share the mitzvah of eating gefilte fish on Shabbos with all the people in town."

Saying this, they began cutting open the fish to get it ready for cooking. All of a sudden, they noticed something very strange. For as they opened the fish and looked inside, they discovered a very large stone. And it wasn't just a plain stone after all. For as Reb Yosef washed the stone, it began to sparkle and shine so brilliantly.

"*Baruch Hashem,*" he called out. "Oh how fortunate we are. Look what Hashem sent us! It must be worth a fortune. Now we'll be able to give more Tzedakah than ever before."

Yes, in return for honoring the Shabbos so nicely, Hashem rewarded them with riches and good fortune. For this fish had swallowed the diamond that fell out of Yivan's hat, and as a miracle from Hashem, this fish was brought to Reb Yosef Mokir Shabbos.

Yes, he bought it in honor of Shabbos and was so nicely rewarded by Hashem. And in exchange for this large diamond, Reb Yosef received enough gold and silver to fill up thirteen rooms. Yes, thirteen rooms filled with gold and silver in return for paying thirteen golden coins for the big fish in honor of the holy day of Shabbos.

As our wise men tell us, He who spends more for Shabbos, the Shabbos will surely repay him in full measure.

THIS IS THE WAY
I WASH
my
HANDS
על נטילת
ידים
אורח חיים, חלק א' סימן ד'

This Is The Way I Wash My Hands

"What are you doing, little Zalman?" asked Mother as she came into the room and found little Zalman standing next to a large basin of water.

Little Zalman looked up and said, "Why Mommy, I'm doing my homework!"

"What kind of homework is that? All I hear is the splashing of water."

"Well, you see, Mommy, we learned something very interesting in class today. Our teacher taught us how to wash *negel vasser*, the ritual washing of the hands, as soon as we get up in the morning."

"Oh, how interesting," said Mother. "Tell me more about it."

"Well, our teacher taught us how to wash our hands in a very special way. And this we do right after we say the *Modeh Ani*. Yes, Mommy, that's what my homework is all about.

"And do you know what our teacher brought to school today? A large bowl, a tall cup with two handles, and a towel. He showed us exactly how to fill the tall cup with water and how to pour the water over our hands. And as a special treat for tomorrow, our teacher said he's going to give us all a chance to wash negel vasser in front of the class."

"Oh how lovely," said Mother. "Let's see what you remember from today's lesson."

"Very well, Mommy, I'll try. It goes like this, first I take the large cup with my right hand and place it into my left hand. Then I pour the water over my right hand, like this."

"Oh how interesting," said Mother. "Please go on."

"Then I take the large cup with my right hand and pour water over my left hand, like this.

"Now, I repeat the same thing until both my hands are washed three times. And to top it all, I also know the *Bracha*, the blessing, for washing negel vasser. It goes like this:

"Baruch Ato Hashem, Elokainu Melech Ho'olam, Asher Kid'shonu B'mitzvosav V'Tzivonu Al N'tilas Yodayim.

"And the meaning to these words are, "Blessed are You, Hashem, our G-d, King of the World, who has made us holy through His commandments, and has commanded us on the washing of the hands."

"And to help us remember this lovely mitzvah, our teacher taught us a new song, and it goes like this:

Modeh Ani L'fonecha, is what I say in the morning.

I wash my hands and then I say, Al Netilas Yodayim.

This is the way I wash my hands.

This is the way I wash my hands.

This is the way I wash my hands, for Netilas Yadayim.

This is the way I wash my hands.

This is the way I wash my hands.

This is the way I wash my hands, for Netilas Yadayim.

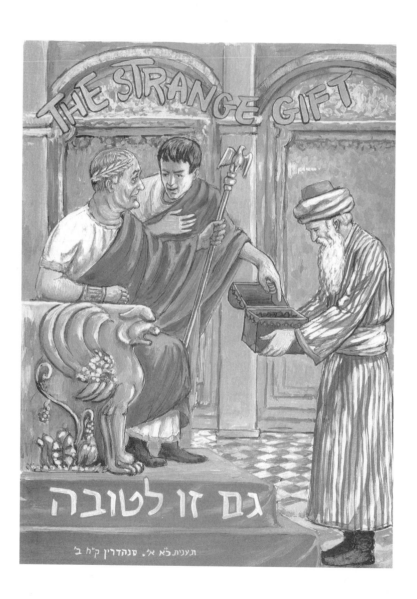

THE STRANGE GIFT

גם זו לטובה

תענית כ"א א'. סנהדרין ק"ח ב'

The Strange Gift

It's eight o'clock in the evening, and for little Yehoshua, it's story time. Little Yehoshua is already in bed waiting for his father to come in to tell him a story.

As his father entered into the room, little Yehoshua looked up and said, "Tatty, today my teacher told me a very interesting story about Avraham Aveinu."

"Oh, that's nice," said Father. "What was it all about?"

"It was about the way Hashem helped him fight off a whole army of soldiers. My teacher said it was a miracle!"

"Oh that sounds so interesting. Tell me, how did he win the war?"

"Well, all Avraham Aveinu did was pick up a handful of dust and a few pieces of straw and he threw it all at the soldiers. And you know what Hashem did? Hashem made the dust turn into arrows, and the pieces of straw became sharp swords. And this is how he won the war. Wow! Wasn't that some miracle, Tatty?"

"Why of course, Yehoshua. You see, Avraham truly believed in Hashem and he knew that Hashem would surely help him in the time of need.

"Now, with Hashem on his side, he didn't need any bows and arrows or swords. All that he really needed was a strong belief and trust in Hashem. No matter how big and strong the enemy may be, with Hashem on our side, we must always be the winners!"

"Oh yes, Tatty, that's so true. And what story do you have for me tonight?"

"Well, I think I'm going to treat you to a special story. In fact, this story is almost like the one you just told me. But it happened many, many years later.

"It's about a very great Tzaddik whose name was Reb Nochum. He was known by all with the name of Reb Nochum Ish Gam Zu. This was because he would so often say, *Gam Zu L'Tova*, which means, this too is for good.

And the story goes like this:

There once was a king who did not permit the Jewish people to learn Torah or to observe any of the mitzvos. So, Reb Nochum Ish Gam Zu was sent to speak to the king to beg him to please be kind to the Jewish people and permit them to learn Hashem's holy Torah and observe its mitzvos.

In order to gain favor in the eyes of the king, Reb Nochum Ish Gam Zu took along a golden box filled to the top with precious diamonds.

On the way, he stopped off at a hotel where he stayed for the night. As he was fast asleep, someone came into his room and took out all the precious diamonds from the golden box and filled it with plain sand.

The next morning, Reb Nochum Ish Gam Zu found out what had happened, and you can guess what he said. That's right, "Gam Zu L'Tova, this too is for good."

He took the golden box filled with sand and continued on his way to the king.

As he arrived at the palace and came before the king, he said, "Your Majesty, I beg you to please permit the Jewish people to continue to learn Torah and observe its mitzvos. And in their name, I wish to present to you this gift."

You can imagine how surprised the king was when he opened the box and saw that it was filled with just plain sand. This made the king very angry; he thought that Reb Nochum was making fun of him. So he ordered that Reb Nochum be thrown into prison and be put to death. To this, Reb Nochum said, "Gam Zu L'Tova, this too is for good."

Now, Hashem, the All Merciful, who is at all times guarding and protecting the Jewish people, sent Eliyahu HaNavi, Elijah the Prophet, to go and help Reb Nochum Ish Gam Zu in this time of need.

Disguised as one of the king's officers, Eliyahu HaNavi called out, "Your Majesty! How can you possibly think that the Jews would want to make fun of you? They surely want you to act kindly towards them. Perhaps the sand they sent you is the miracle sand, the same sand that Abraham used against his enemies. Why not take this sand to the battlefield and use it on our enemies? Let's see what will happen to them."

The king agreed and to the surprise of his generals, he ordered that the sand be used against their enemies on the battlefield. And you know what happened? A miracle took place and the battle was quickly won.

Upon seeing this, the king called for Reb Nochum Ish Gam Zu and thanked him for the unusual gift. He told him that the Jewish people may continue to serve Hashem through the study of the Torah and the observance of the mitzvos.

The king then ordered that the golden box be filled with the most valuable treasures, and he sent Reb Nochum back home with high honor.

On his way home, Reb Nochum stopped off to rest at the same hotel as before. Now, it was the owner of the hotel who stole the diamonds from the golden box and filled it with sand. So when he heard about the great reward given to Reb Nochum, he asked him, "What did you give to the king that he rewarded you so richly?"

"I gave him the golden box, " said Reb Nochum. Upon hearing this, the owner of the hotel ordered his workers to throw down the hotel and help him carry all the sand to the king.

"Your Majesty," said the hotel keeper, "I have brought to you wagon loads of the very same sand which Reb Nochum brought to you, the sand which you value so much."

"Is that so?" said the king, curiously. "Well, we shall see. Tomorrow we will try it on the battlefield."

And guess what happened — it turned out to be just plain sand! The king realized what the hotel keeper did and ordered that he be put to death for his crime.

And do you know what Reb Nochum Ish Gam Zu said when he heard about it? That's right, he said "Gam Zu L'Tova, this too is for good."

"Oh, thank you, Tatty, for this lovely story!" said little Yehoshua. "Now, I have another new story to tell my friends in class."

"Wonderful," said Father, "and don't forget to tell them the wonderful lesson we learn from it. That is, as Reb Nochum Ish Gam Zu said, always remember 'Gam Zu L'Tova.' That means that all that Hashem does is so truly good."

After his father tucked him into bed and kissed him goodnight, little Yehoshua said the Shema Yisroel and fell fast asleep.

Hashem Is Good

Hashem is good and all that He does is good. Hashem, the one and only G-d who created the heavens and earth, is purely good, and nothing bad can come from Him.

The Talmud teaches us how Rabbi Akiva would so often say, *"Kol Mah D'ovid Rachmono L'tav Ovid.* All that Hashem does, He does for good."

True, there are times when it is hard for us to understand and truly realize that everything Hashem does is good. Yet, sooner or later, we find out that it was for our own good.

The Talmud tells us of a strange but interesting story that happened to Rabbi Akiva as he was traveling on the road.

Whenever Rabbi Akiva would travel, he would take along three things: a donkey, a rooster, and a candle.

The donkey would carry all of his belongings. The rooster would wake him up in time to pray. And the candle was to give him light during the dark hours of the night so that he may pray and continue the study of Torah late into the night.

The sun was about to set and Rabbi Akiva headed for a nearby town where he planned to stay overnight. But as he entered into the town, he couldn't find anyone who would be kind enough to invite him into their house for the night. This meant, of course, that Rabbi Akiva would have to spend the night all alone in the forest.

Upon realizing this, Rabbi Akiva looked up to the heaven and said, *"Kol Mah D'ovid Rachmono L'tav Ovid*, all that Hashem does, He does for good."

Upon saying this, Rabbi Akiva turned back and headed for the forest. By the time Rabbi Akiva returned to the forest, it was already very dark.

He selected a place off the road where he planned to spend the night. He took off the load which was tied on the back of the donkey, fed the donkey some food and set it to rest for the night. All was peaceful and quiet, as Rabbi Akiva lit the candle and with the light of its flickering flame, sat down to learn Torah.

All of a sudden, a very strong wind came and blew out the flame, leaving Rabbi Akiva in total darkness. Upon seeing this, Rabbi Akiva looked up to the heaven and said, *"Kol Mah D'ovid Rachmono L'tav Ovid*. All that Hashem does, He does for good."

A few moments later, out of the forest came a hungry lion and ate up the donkey. And to top it all, along came a cat and ate up the rooster.

You probably can guess what Rabbi Akiva said to all this. That's right, *"Kol Mah D'ovid Rachmono L'tav Ovid. All that Hashem does, He does for good."*

The next morning, as Rabbi Akiva arrived in the nearby town, he found out that during the night, a band of wicked robbers came out of the forest and entered into the town where they robbed the people of all their belongings.

It was then that Rabbi Akiva realized how true it really was that all that Hashem does, He does for good, for if the people of town would have invited him to stay in their house for the night he, too, would have been robbed of all his belongings. He also realized that the wicked robbers would have surely noticed him in the forest by the flickering flame of the candle, and the sounds made by the donkey and rooster.

The Talmud teaches us this story so that we may learn an important lesson from it. We, too, must know that nothing happens by accident or chance, and that nothing happens without Hashem knowing it.

Yes, Hashem is truly good, and whatever He does, He does for good. And though at times it may be difficult to realize right away how truly good are the ways of Hashem, sooner or later we find out that it was for our own good.

So remember, *"Kol Mah D'ovid Rachmono L'tav Ovid*, all that Hashem does, He does for good!"

THE SOUND OF THE SHOFAR

The Sound of the Shofar

Hashem commanded us in the Torah to sound the Shofar, which is a ram's horn, on Rosh Hashana, the Jewish New Year. As it is written in the Torah, "*Yom T'ruah Yih-yeh Lochem*, it is a day during which you are to sound the Shofar."

The great rabbi, the Rambam, of blessed memory, explained: although the Torah gives no reason why we are to blow the Shofar on Rosh Hashana, it is a heavenly decree, yet there are many lessons that are hinted in this lovely mitzvah.

Above all, the sounds of the Shofar are compared to an alarm, which wakes up a person from his sleep. So the same it is with the Shofar. These holy sounds are to awaken us and remind us that today is Rosh Hashana, the beginning of the New Year. It is on this day that we all proclaim that Hashem is our king and we are His servants. He is our Father and we are His children.

The sounds of the Shofar are to remind us that it is on this holy day that we are to pray to Hashem that He inscribe us all in the *Sefer Hachayim*, the Book of Life. We do Teshuvah, we repent all our wrong-doings, and firmly resolve to better our ways by learning Torah and observing Hashem's holy mitzvos. And Hashem, in His great kindness, accepts our prayers and blesses us all with good health, true joy, and fortune for the entire coming year. He grants us all a *Shana Tova U'mesuka,* a good and sweet year both in body and in spirit.

In order to understand this more clearly, I will tell you a story.

Once a fire broke out in a village and many homes were burnt down to the ground. All that was left was a heap of ashes. It took a long time until the village people managed to build a new home.

But alas, again a fire broke out, and before the people had a chance to battle the blaze, the flames had already leaped from one home to the other. A large number of homes were burnt down to the ground, leaving so many people homeless.

The village people were desperately seeking a solution to this serious problem. They called a public meeting to discuss the matter. Perhaps someone will come up with an idea as how to prevent these disasters from striking again.

After a long discussion, the village people finally came up with a brilliant idea. They all decided to have someone travel to a big city and find out what the people do there whenever there is a fire. They agreed to pay all traveling expenses, but needed someone to volunteer to take the trip.

After a few moments of silence, a young farmer boy stood up and said that he was ready to travel to the big city. He had never been there before and had been waiting for this opportunity for such a long time.

All the people of the village agreed, and early the next morning, the farmer boy was on his way to the big city.

As the farmer boy arrived in the big city, he asked the people, "What do you do in a big city when there is a fire?"

The people brought him over to the nearest fire station and introduced him to the fire chief. Upon hearing the farmer boy's question, the fire chief said, "Come, young boy, I'll show you."

Saying this, the fire chief took out a long bugle and said, "Come, please follow me outside."

As they were both outside, the fire chief pointed upwards and said, "See this tall tower? Well, as soon as there's a fire, I take this bugle and climb all the way up to the top of this tower. Then I blow into this bugle with all my might, loudly and clearly, so that everyone can hear it."

The farmer boy leaped for joy and called out, "Oh thank you, Sir! Thank you so very much for helping me. But can you please tell me where can I get a bugle just like the one you have?"

The fire chief showed him exactly where to buy the very same bugle. The farmer boy bought the bugle, and filled with joy, started on his trip back to the village to share the good news with everyone. He felt so lucky for now he knew what to do in case a fire ever breaks out again.

There was so much excitement in the village, and the farmer boy returned and told all the people the good news, that now he knows how to put out a fire just like the people do in the big city. The people of the village cheered and applauded.

The farmer boy instructed the people to build a very tall tower right at the center of the marketplace, and as soon as the tower will be ready he will be able to show them what the people do in the big city whenever there is a fire.

A few days later, the village people completed building the tall tower.

Now, all was quiet and peaceful in the village when all of a sudden, one day, a fire broke out, and in a moment's notice, the farmer boy was seen climbing up the tall tower with a long bugle in his hand. All the people gathered around the tower to see the great spectacle.

In total suspense, they all stood around motionless, as they watched the farmer boy reach to the very top of the tower.

Quickly, the farmer boy took out the long bugle and began to blow as hard as he can. But as he blew louder and louder, the flames kept on jumping higher and higher until, alas, an entire row of houses was burnt down to the ground. All that was left was a heap of ashes.

Totally disappointed and deeply embarrassed, the farmer boy climbed down the tall tower and began to cry bitterly, "I can't understand it! I can't understand it! What did I do wrong? I did exactly what the fire chief told me to do. Why didn't the fire go out? I must return to the big city and ask the fire chief why I failed to put out the fire."

Saying this, he tucked the long bugle under his arm and started on his trip, back to the big city.

As the fire chief heard the farmer boy's sad story, he called out, "What? Is that all you did? You just blew the bugle? Oh, how foolish! The bugle can't put out the fire! The sounds of the bugle are only to alarm and signal the people that there is a fire. It's a signal for them to run and get water and put out the fire."

Yes, from this story we can learn one of the important reasons why the Shofar is sounded on Rosh Hashana. It is an alarm to awaken us and an alarm for action.

For the sounds of the Shofar are to remind us that today is Rosh Hashana and we are being judged by Hashem, the All Merciful.

All our thoughts, words, and actions are being judged and weighed on the heavenly scale. The sounds of the Shofar are calling to us and saying, "There are three things for us to do in order to find grace in the eyes of Hashem. They are *Teshuvah*, repentance; *Tefilah*, prayer; and *Tzedakah*, charity."

We firmly trust and believe that by doing this, Hashem will surely bless us all with a full year of good health, happiness, and fortune, and above all, a year of shalom, true and everlasting peace. A year during which we shall witness the sounding of the Shofar Gadol, the big Shofar that Hashem Himself will blow.

It will signal the arrival of our righteous Redeemer, *Moshiach Tzidkeinu*, who will return us all to our holy land, Eretz Yisroel.

L'shono Habo'o B'Yerusholayim. By next year, we shall all surely be in Yerushalayim.

The Secret of the Empty Fireplace

Here is a story about a little boy called Menachem Mendel. He was truly an unusual child. While yet in his young years, he already had a glowing flame of love for Hashem and His holy Torah. He found no greater pleasure in life than to learn more and more Torah.

It was no surprise that little Menachem Mendel later grew up to be a great and famous rabbi known to all as the Tzemach Tzedek, of blessed memory.

Now his grandfather, the famous Rabbi Schneur Zalman, known better as the Rav or the Alter Rebbe, would often invite his children into his own study and privately teach them Torah. However, little Menachem Mendel was too young to attend these sessions in learning. He was only nine years old. And for this reason, he wasn't invited to join this group in learning Torah.

He truly envied those who were so fortunate to learn Torah with his grandfather. He felt that he would be the luckiest person on earth if he could only learn Torah with his holy grandfather.

In the Alter Rebbe's home there were two large rooms. One of the rooms was used as the Alter Rebbe's private study, and the other was used as a waiting room. The two rooms were separated by a very thick wall and in the wall there was a large fireplace which was used to provide heat for both rooms the whole winter season. They would place many logs of wood into the fireplace and set them afire, but during the summertime, the fireplace remained empty.

Little Menachem Mendel came up with a grand idea. He thought to himself, "Since I'm not permitted to enter my grandfather's room to learn Torah, perhaps there is a way to listen to him teach Torah without entering into the room."

You can guess what he decided to do. That's right, he went into the waiting room and slowly opened the gate to the fireplace and was so thrilled to find it empty.

Carefully and quietly, he crawled into the fireplace, and lo and behold, he was now able to hear clearly all the Torah the Alter Rebbe was teaching.

Now this kept up for quite a while. Every time the Alter Rebbe would invite his children into his private study to teach them Torah, little Menachem Mendel managed to be there listening to the Torah from inside the empty fireplace. No one at all knew of this clever plan, for little Menachem Mendel kept it a secret.

One evening, as the Alter Rebbe was teaching Torah to his children in his private study, and little Menachem Mendel was listening in from the empty fireplace, the butler was called in to place logs of wood into the fireplace and set them afire. Yes, it suddenly became cold and they decided to use the fireplace to warm up the house.

Little Menachem Mendel was so busy listening to every word of the Alter Rebbe's Torah that he didn't even notice how the butler began pushing logs of wood right next to him. He was so engrossed in the learning of Torah that he didn't even feel what was happening.

Well, you can imagine what took place as soon as the butler began to set the logs on fire. For suddenly, the burning logs began flying out of the fireplace very wildly. From seeing the burning logs shooting out of the fireplace, the butler began to scream for help. He was so frightened. He just couldn't figure out what was happening.

In a moment's notice, everyone came into the room to see what the excitement was all about. As they went over to the fireplace, they were all so shocked to see little Menachem Mendel lying there motionless. They all began to cry, "Menachem Mendel! Menachem Mendel!" But there came no answer.

Carefully, they pulled him out of the fireplace and tried to awaken him. But in spite of all their efforts, they just couldn't revive him.

Everything seemed quite hopeless until in came the Alter Rebbe and gently placed his hand on the head of little Menachem Mendel, and at that very moment little Menachem Mendel awoke and opened his eyes. Everyone called out, "Menachem Mendel is alive! *Baruch Hashem*! What a miracle!"

Yes, little Menachem Mendel's love for Torah was so great that he was ready to do anything just to learn more and more Torah, even until *mesiras nefesh*, self-sacrifice. He was even ready to give up his own life for the sake of Torah.

Just like the very first Jew, Avraham Aveinu, showed his loyalty to Hashem by permitting himself to be thrown into a fiery furnace, and just like Moshe Rabbeinu reached Har Sinai and through him the Torah was given to B'nei Yisroel, the Children of Israel, only after he witnessed the heavenly fire in the burning bush, the same refers to us.

We are to realize that they have set themselves as an example for all generations to come. We are to follow them, just like little Menachem Mendel did, and do all in our power to learn more and more Torah. And in return, Hashem will surely bless us all with good health, long life, and total success both in body and in spirit.

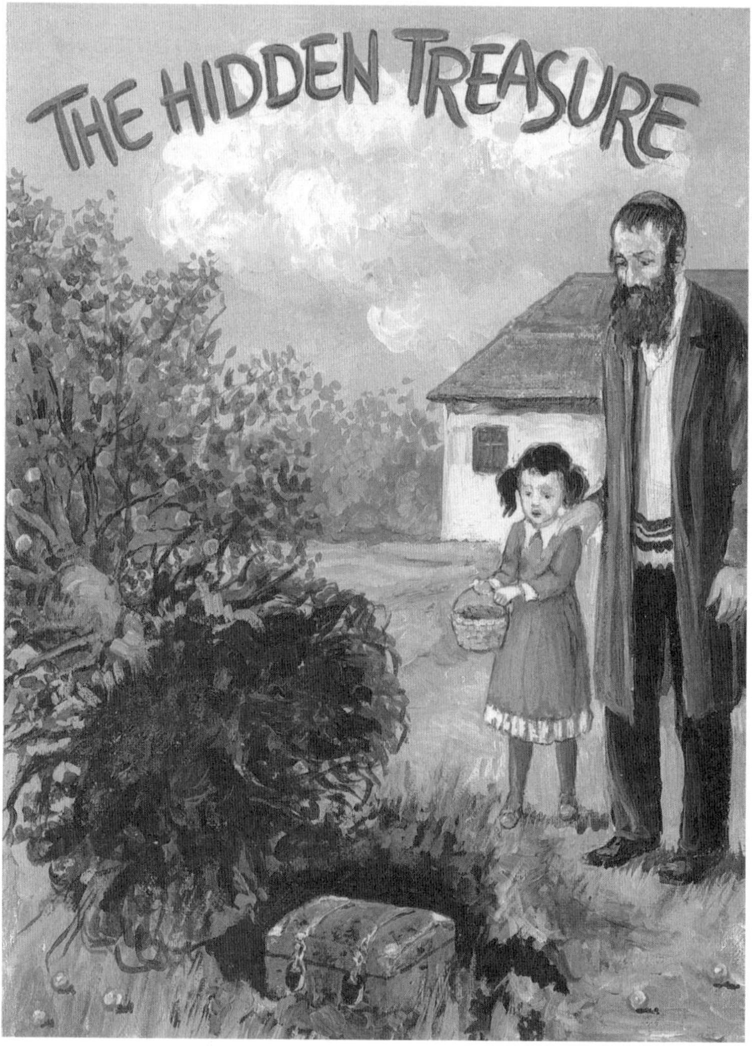
THE HIDDEN TREASURE

The Hidden Treasure

There are 613 mitzvos, commandments, in the holy Torah. From all of these mitzvos, we find one mitzvah in particular that is truly outstanding. That is, the mitzvah of Tzedakah, charity.

The mitzvah of Tzedakah is so greatly treasured in the eyes of Hashem that in the merit of giving Tzedakah, our Righteous Redeemer, Moshiach Tzidkeinu, will come and free us all from golus, exile. As our Sages say, *"Ein Yisroel Nig'olin Ela B'Tzedakah. The redemption of the Jewish people will come only through the merit of Tzedakah."*

Yes, we must realize that each time we give Tzedakah by placing a coin into the Tzedakah box or by giving Tzedakah to a poor person, we cause Moshiach to come that much sooner.

Here is a lovely story about a young girl who loved to give Tzedakah. Her name was Sarah.

Sarah was a fine Jewish girl. Everyone admired her for her unusual kindness and good heart. She truly loved the mitzvah of Tzedakah with all her heart. She was so glad to share her own belongings with all who were in need.

Though Sarah's parents weren't rich at all, in fact, her father worked so very hard and barely managed to support his family, yet he never failed to spare a few pennies to give to Sarah as a daily treat.

Rarely would Sarah use these pennies for herself. Instead, she would place some of the coins into her own Tzedakah box and the rest she would give to the poor beggars she would find in the street. Sarah would always bless the beggars with good fortune, each time she gave them some Tzedakah.

Yes, Sarah truly enjoyed giving Tzedakah. She knew that all of Hashem's heavenly blessings will reach her in full measure through the great mitzvah of Tzedakah.

Even when times became very difficult, Sarah would seek ways to practice the mitzvah of Tzedakah in any manner possible. Her father would often comfort her by saying, "Sarale, *Vos Der Eibishter Tut, Iz Goot.* Sarah, whatever Hashem does is good."

Now, right in the back of Sarah's house there stood a tall apple tree, and this was no ordinary tree at all. For the apples of this tree were the most juicy and delicious apples in town. And as soon as the apples were ripe and ready, little Sarah would pick them off the tree and place them into a yellow basket. Then she would visit the poor families who lived nearby and ofter them delicious apples.

110

In appreciation for this kind deed, the poor people would bless her and thank her, and in return Sarah would say, "Oh please, don't thank me, thank Hashem, for Hashem created the trees and the delicious apples."

In fact, she used to help them recite the *Bracha*, the blessing, over the apples, until they knew how to say the Bracha all by themselves.

One night, there was a fierce storm. It began to rain very heavily and the winds kept on blowing stronger and stronger. Loud roars of thunder and bright flashes of lightning continued endlessly throughout the night.

Early the next morning, Sarah looked out of the window and cried out, "Oh Tatty, please come here quickly! Look what happened!" Her father rushed over to the window to see what had happened. And alas, he stood there motionless.

"Oh my!" he called out. "The apple tree! The apple tree!"

Yes, the tall apple tree had been blown down to the ground by the stormy winds.

Little Sarah looked up to her father and cried, "What am I going to tell these poor families? Now I will have no more apples to give them."

Upon hearing this, her father took out his handkerchief and gently wiped the tears from Sarah's face, and then said to her, "Sarale, don't you remember? *Vos Der Eibishter Tut, Iz Goot.* Whatever Hashem does is good. There surely must be a good reason why Hashem did this."

"Where are you going, Sarah?" asked Father, as he noticed her take her yellow basket and head for the door.

Sarale looked up and answered, "I would just love to have one more chance to help those poor children. Surely there must be some good apples left on the ground for me to pick up. I hope there will be enough to fill up my yellow basket so that I can do the mitzvah of Tzedakah one more time." Saying this, Sara left the room and headed for the fallen apple tree.

But as soon as Sarah came close to the tree, she called out, "Oh Tatty! Oh Tatty, please come quickly!"

Her father came running out and said, "What now, dear Sarale?"

"Oh look here, Tatty! Right in that big hole!"

Her father took one look and called out, "Oh my! *Baruch Hashem*! It looks like a hidden treasure!"

Yes, when the tree fell down, its roots tore a big hole in the ground. Right there before their eyes, was a hidden treasure.

You can imagine how surprised they were. When they opened it up, they found it to be filled to the top with diamonds, gems, jewels, gold, and silver — a fortune of wealth, indeed!

Sarah called out, "Thank you, Hashem! Now we can give more Tzedakah than ever before!"

Sarale looked up to her father and said, "Yes, Tatty, it's so true, *'Vos Der Eibishter Tut, Iz Goot.* Whatever Hashem does, is good!'"

Yes, remember how important the mitzvah of Tzedakah is. For each time you place Tzedakah into the Tzedakah box, remember Hashem is there watching you, and in return for your kindness, blesses you with great reward, both on this world and in the World to Come.

A Peek at the Third Beis HaMikdash

"Mommy! Mommy! Where are you?" called little Levi, as he came home from school filled with excitement.

"I'm here, right in the kitchen, dear Levi. Why are you so excited? What happened?"

"Oh Mommy, I must tell you what my rabbi taught me today in the Yeshiva. It's something really new. I never learned this before."

"Go right ahead, please tell me. I would like to know what it's all about," Mother answered.

"Well, my Rebbe told me that way up in the sky Hashem built a *Beis HaMikdash*, a holy temple. And when the right time comes, Hashem is going to lower the new Beis HaMikdash right down from heaven and set it on the top of Har HaMoriah in Yerushalayim, the very same mountain where the first and second Beis HaMikdash stood many, many years ago.

"Oh Mommy, I'm so excited because my Rebbe also said that each time I learn Torah, daven (pray), or do any mitzvah, Hashem keeps lowering the Beis HaMikdash more and more until all of a sudden everyone will be able to see it. I just can't wait for Tatty to come home today. I'd love to tell him what I learned in the Yeshiva. Maybe he can also teach me some more things about the third Beis HaMikdash."

As soon as Father came home, Levi ran over excitedly and told him the good news.

As soon as his father heard this, he called out, "Why of course, dear Levi, I want you to know that the third Beis HaMikdash is going to remain here forever. You see, the first Beis HaMikdash was built by people and destroyed by people, and the same with the second Beis HaMikdash. But the third Beis HaMikdash is going to remain forever because it was built by Hashem himself!"

Little Levi looked up at his father and said, "Oh if I could only take a peek at the new Beis HaMikdash, wow, that would be some treat. Just imagine how beautiful and magnificent it must be. After all, it's built by Hashem Himself!"

"True, dear Levi," Father answered. "But you have to be a real Tzaddik to be able to get a peek at the third Beis HaMikdash."

"What?" called out Levi. "You mean to say that Hashem shows the Beis HaMikdash to the Tzaddikim?"

"Yes, dear Levi. In fact, I'm going to let you in on a secret. A very great Tzaddik named Rabbi Levi Yitzchok from the city of Berdichev said that once a year during the Shabbos that is called *"Shabbos Chazon,"* Hashem permits the Tzaddikim to take a peek at the third Beis HaMikdash.

"You see, Shabbos Chazon is the Shabbos that comes right before Tisha B'Av, the 9th day of the month of Av. It was during this day that the first and second Beis HaMikdash were destroyed. Today, we fast on Tisha B'Av to remember the destruction of the Beis HaMikdash and pray to Hashem to rebuild it and send Moshiach Tzidkeinu to us, and return us all to Eretz Yisroel."

"Continue, continue," called out Levi. "Tell me some more."

"Oh, I'm sorry, dear Levi. It's time for you to go to sleep. You have to get up early tomorrow morning to go to the Yeshiva."

Little Levi prepared his *negel vasser* right next to his bed, that is, the basin and the large cup of water to use to wash his hands in the morning, and he began to recite the Shema. A few minutes later, his father came into his bedroom to kiss him good-night. His father said, "Pleasant dreams, Levi," as he walked out of the room and closed the door.

But little Levi just couldn't fall asleep, and you can guess what he was thinking about — that's right, the third Beis HaMikdash.

There he was, lying in bed, looking out of the window, carefully studying the sparkling stars as they twinkled from way up high. All of a sudden, Levi heard someone calling, "Your attention please! Your attention please! Flight number 770 is ready for takeoff, flight number 770 is ready for takeoff. All passengers are asked to please board the spaceship right now. The countdown for blast off will be at any moment. Please hurry, please hurry."

Levi jumped out of bed to see where the sounds were coming from. As he looked out of his bedroom window he just couldn't believe his eyes. For there, right in his backyard, was a very big spaceship and it was ready for takeoff.

Filled with excitement, little Levi called out, "Please wait for me! Please wait for me! I'm coming!" Levi tiptoed out of the house and ran towards the big spaceship.

"Please wait!" he called out as loud as he could, as he ran up the long and winding stairway, leading to the door of the cabin.

"Welcome aboard, Levi." the captain said. "You just made it on time. Hurry, here is your spacesuit. Follow me this way."

Quickly, Levi put on his spacesuit and fastened his seat belt as the rocket roared out into space...

A few moments later, little Levi called to the captain and said, "Can you please head towards the direction of the third Beis HaMikdash? I would love to visit it!"

The captain smiled, thought for a while and said, "Yes, that's possible, but only on one condition. You shouldn't spend too much time there. You see, we must have enough fuel to fly back to earth."

"Oh thank you!" Levi called out. "I'll try to be as quick as possible."

It didn't take long and the captain called out, "Okay, Levi, here we are! Look out of the window and you can see it."

Levi jumped out of his seat and screamed, "Oh my! There's the third Beis HaMikdash! Oh look at it! So big. It's so beautiful. I never saw anything like this before in my life. I just can't wait to go out and visit the third Beis HaMikdash."

As the cabin door opened and little Levi was just about ready to head for the third Beis HaMikdash, the captain looked at his watch and said, "Remember, Levi, be as quick as possible. Please make sure to return to the ship in no later than seven minutes."

"Very well, very well," said Levi as he stepped onto the soft clouds and headed towards the third Beis HaMikdash.

As he stood there marveling at the beautiful sight, he didn't realize that time was running out.

Seven minutes had already passed. Suddenly, he heard a large roaring sound, he turned around quickly and alas, the spaceship was taking off. It was heading back to earth.

He began to cry, "Oh please. Don't go away! Wait for me! I want to go home. Don't leave me here alone. Please come back. I want to go home. I want to go home!"

"What's the matter, dear Levi? Why are you crying?" Mother called out.

Levi opened his eyes, looked around, and found Mommy and Tatty standing right next to his bed.

"Oh my — it was only a dream. It was only a dream! I just can't believe it, Mommy. I dreamt that I saw the third Beis HaMikdash. Oh boy will you be surprised when I tell you what I saw in my dream, and I just can't wait until I get back to school and tell this to my teacher. Boy, will he be surprised."

Yes, to Levi it was only a dream. A good dream indeed. But I'd like to let you know that we can all make this dream come true. That's right, we can hurry up the coming of Moshiach and the lowering of the Beis HaMikdash.

All we have to do is learn more and more Torah and do more and more mitzvos, and in return, Hashem will surely bless us all, and we will witness with our own eyes the third Beis HaMikdash, *Bimhayra V'yamaynu*, speedily in our days, Amen!

The Mystery of Dayeinu

It is the night of Pesach and the entire family is gathered around the beautifully set table to take part in the Seder.

We read the Haggadah and tell about the many wonders and miracles Hashem did for us, how Hashem took us out of the land of Egypt where we were slaves for so many years.

Throughout the night, we sing songs of praise and thanks to Hashem for all His kindness. And of all of the songs we sing at the Seder, there is one song that is truly outstanding. That is the lovely song called Dayeinu, for in it we find mentioned so many miracles and wonders that Hashem did for us.

Here is an interesting story about a very kind-hearted Jew called Reb Sholom and how Hashem helped him through a miracle. Strangely enough, the miracle took place Pesach night at the Seder as Reb Sholom was singing the lovely song Dayeinu.

And the story goes like this. In our holy Torah, we find so many lovely mitzvos. Some of them teach us how to be honest or how to be kind, how to be well mannered, or how to treat our fellow man. Yes, each mitzvah has its own way in helping us becoming better and better, from day to day, so that we may serve Hashem in truth, with all our heart and with all our soul.

Now, of all of these lovely mitzvos we find one that is so truly outstanding and that is the mitzvah of *Hachnasas Orchim*, to invite guests into our home. For through this mitzvah, we have a wonderful chance to be kind to our fellow man in so many different ways. We feed them delicious food, we provide them with a comfortable bed in which to sleep and relax, and as they leave, we bid them farewell, and bless them with all good.

And this is the mitzvah that Reb Sholom was so famous for. His love to the mitzvah of Hachnasas Orchim was truly unusual. Just like the house of Avraham Aveinu, Abraham our Father, and Sarah Emeinu, Sarah our Mother, Reb Sholom's house was always filled with guests, especially on Shabbos and Yom Tov, the holidays when so many poor people would turn to Reb Sholom for help.

Now, Reb Sholom wasn't the richest man in town after all. In fact, there were times when Reb Sholom found it quite difficult to support his own family and yet at the same time continue to provide all the needs of the many guests. He would then turn to Hashem in prayer to help him carry out this lovely mitzvah. And the All-Merciful Hashem would always answer his prayers in one way or another.

It was before Pesach and Reb Sholom was busy preparing for the Yom Tov, when all of a sudden he realized that there were many more guests coming for Yom Tov than usual.

"Oh my!" he cried. "How will I ever manage to buy so much food for all those guests?"

Reb Sholom felt very sad. He was afraid that he may have to disappoint some of the poor and hungry guests. He may have to turn them down and this is something he had never done before. With a saddened heart, he took out the Tehillim and began to pray to Hashem.

"Oh please help me!" Reb Sholom cried. "It is not for my own sake that I am praying to you, but for the sake of those poor and hungry people."

Now, little did Reb Sholom realize that while he was praying to Hashem for help, a great miracle was already in the making. For all of a sudden he heard people shouting in the streets, "The king has lost his ring! The king has lost his ring! Anyone who will find it will receive ten thousand gold pieces as a reward."

Upon hearing this, Reb Sholom went to the king to offer his help to find the ring. "Your Majesty," he said. "I will gather all the members of my community and ask them all to help search for the lost ring."

The king was so glad to hear Reb Sholom's kind offer that he took out a large sack of gold coins and said, "Here, Reb Sholom. I know that you have a good heart. You're always giving charity to the poor. Please accept this sack of gold. I'm sure that you can make good use of it."

Reb Sholom just stood there motionless. He couldn't believe his eyes, for now he had all the money he needed to buy plenty of food for the poor and needy guests.

Days have passed and there was no trace or clue as to where the lost ring may be. It seemed to have disappeared into thin air and this made the king so very sad.

Now, in order to cheer up the king and make him happy again, the queen suggested that they pay a visit to the house of Reb Sholom during the night of Pesach. She knew of the special way Reb Sholom celebrated the Pesach, how he invites so many poor people to take part in the beautiful Seder.

Yes, the queen felt sure that the happy surroundings, the festive mood, and the joyful singing will surely cheer up the king and make him happy again.

Strangely enough, the king agreed to leave the royal palace and pay a visit to Reb Sholom on the night of Pesach.

The night of Pesach finally arrived and Reb Sholom's house was filled with guests who were taking part in the great Seder. The voices of their singing could be heard for quite a distance.

Now, just as the king came close to Reb Sholom's house, his face lit up in joy as he just stood there listening to the lovely songs sung at the Seder. Suddenly, he turned to the queen and said, "Do you hear what they are saying? Why they are all calling out Dayeinu!"

Curiously, the king peeked through the window to see what was going on. And to his surprise, there was Reb Sholom at the head of the table and all the guests around him were calling out Dayeinu.

Filled with excitement, the king said, "I understand. Reb Sholom must have asked them who has the ring. And all of them answered Dayeinu. Oh my, I must go back to the palace immediately and find out if it is true, for Dayeinu is the name of one of my servants."

You can imagine how surprised the king was when his servant Dayeinu admitted that he had the ring.

Yes, a miracle did take place, for the king awarded Reb Sholom the ten thousand gold pieces for helping him find the ring. It was then that Reb Sholom realized that it was Hashem's answer to his prayers.

In return for his kind heart and the wonderful mitzvah of Hachnasas Orchim, Hashem rewarded Reb Sholom in such a wonderful way. Reb Sholom thanked Hashem and said, *"Baruch Hashem.* Now I can give more Tzedakah than ever before!"

The Cup of Eliyahu HaNavi

Ani Ma'amin, I believe, *B'emunah Sh'layma,* in complete faith, *B'vi-as HaMoshiach,* in the coming of Moshiach.

Moshiach will be a person sent by Hashem Himself. He will gather all the children of Israel from the four corners of the earth and return us all to our own land, our holy land, Eretz Yisroel.

Every Jew truly believes in the coming of Moshiach. In our daily prayers, we ask Hashem to please send us Moshiach right away. Yes, we want Moshiach now.

And our Chachamim, our Sages, tell us that Hashem had selected Eliyahu HaNavi, Elijah the Prophet, to be the one to bring us the good news that Moshiach is finally coming.

In fact, when Pesach comes, we place a special cup filled with wine right in the center of the Seder table. This is in honor of Eliyahu HaNavi. We call it the *"Kos Shel Eliyahu HaNavi,"* the cup of Elijah the

Prophet. For our Sages tell us, that Eliyahu HaNavi visits every Jewish home during the Seder nights and blesses us with all good.

It is during the Seder nights that we ask Hashem to free us once again, just as He freed us from slavery in the land of Egypt so many years ago.

We all call out together, *"L'shana Haba'a B'Yerushalayim,"* that by the coming year we will surely be in our holy city, Yerushalayim, Jerusalem, where the third *Beis HaMikdash* will already be there built by Hashem Himself.

Here is an interesting story about a fine Jewish woman called Devorah and how she honored the Kos Shel Eliyahu HaNavi in such a special way. And in return for this, a miracle took place through which she was so greatly rewarded.

And the story goes like this. The Kos Shel Eliyahu HaNavi that Devorah had was really something so very special. It was a tall cup made out of pure gold, and decorated with so many sparkling diamonds and colorful jewels. To Devorah, this cup was truly a priceless treasure, for it was handed down in her family from generation to generation.

Right before Pesach, she would polish the cup and make it shine so brightly for the Seder nights. She would fill the cup with delicious wine and place it right in the center of the Seder table. All of this was done in the honor of Eliyahu HaNavi.

Now, Devorah's husband, Beryl, was a very devoted and hardworking man. He tried his best to support his family, yet from all of his earnings he hardly had enough to feed his wife and children.

It was before Pesach, and Beryl realized that he just didn't have enough money to buy all that was needed for the holiday.

When he told this to his wife, she said, "Don't worry. Let's trust in Hashem. He will surely help us."

There was a moment of silence and all of a sudden, Beryl called out, "Devorah! I just thought of an idea. Now, if you will take my advice I think we will have plenty of money for a long time to come."

"What do you mean?" said Devorah in surprise. "What are you talking about?"

"Well, we still have that Kos Shel Eliyahu HaNavi, and that must be worth a fortune. Just imagine how rich we will be if we will sell it."

"Oh no!" called out Devorah, "Heaven forbid! We can't do that. Why this Kos was made in the honor of Eliyahu HaNavi, we have no right to sell it. Why, just imagine how Eliyahu HaNavi will feel when he will visit our home during the Seder nights and the cup will no longer be there. We just can't do that. I'm sure that there must be a better way through which Hashem could help us."

A few days passed and there came a fierce rainstorm. Beryl was away at work and Devorah was home taking care of the children.

All of a sudden, she heard a knocking at the door. As Devorah opened the door, she saw an old beggar crying.

"Oh please, have mercy. Permit me to come in. It's raining so hard outside and I'm soaked through and through."

"Why, of course. Do come in," said Devorah. "Here, sit down next to the fireplace and make yourself comfortable, I'm going to prepare a hot drink for you."

"Oh thank you so much," said the old beggar, "You are such a kind lady. Hashem will surely reward you for your kindness."

As soon as the rains stopped, the old beggar got up and said to Devorah, "Before I leave, I would like to bless you. Is there any special blessing you would like to have?" Devorah looked at the old beggar and began to cry.

"What's the matter, dear lady? Why are you crying?"

Devorah looked up and began telling him the sad story about the Kos Shel Eliyahu HaNavi, how much she treasured it, and that her husband Beryl wants to sell it.

"Please bless us," Devorah said. "That Hashem will answer our prayers so that we won't have to sell the cup, after all, it was made in honor of Eliyahu HaNavi."

The old man blessed Devorah with good health and lots of fortune, and as he left, he gave her a golden coin and said, "Here. Please take this. I am sure that you could make good use of it."

After thanking the old beggar and bidding him farewell, she ran over to the grocery to buy some food for the family.

As she returned home with the groceries, she noticed something very strange. For there on the table, right before her eyes, was the golden coin.

"Oh my! How could this be? I forgot to pay the grocer for the food."

But as she returned to the store to apologize, the storekeeper looked at her and said, "I don't understand you. You certainly did pay. Why here's the golden coin that you gave me. You must have had two golden coins. Now, is there anything else you'd like to buy?"

Well, you can imagine how happy Devorah was knowing that now she was able to buy even more food for her family, and you can guess what happened when she returned home. That's right, there was the golden coin right on the table.

Devorah just couldn't believe her eyes. And this kept on happening again and again.

It was then that she realized that the old man really wasn't a beggar after all, but a heavenly messenger in disguise sent by Hashem to help her as an answer to her prayers.

"I wonder if he was Eliyahu HaNavi," Devorah thought to herself. "I really wonder."

Yes, Devorah didn't have to sell the Kos shel Eliyahu HaNavi after all. For now she had all the money she needed for the holiday with so much left over for a long time to come. And you can imagine how excited Beryl was when he came home and heard the good news!

But the real surprise was yet to come. For Pesach night, during the Seder, the same old man came to visit them once more, but this time he introduced himself as Eliyahu HaNavi.

"May Hashem bless you for your good heart and kindness," he said. "And especially for the way you honored my Kos."

As Eliyahu HaNavi was about to leave, Devorah called out, "Please come once more and bring us the good news that Moshiach is coming now." To this he answered, "Very well. Very well. And I'd like to let you in on a secret, it is much sooner than you think!"

The Tall
Chanukah Candles

Did you ever see a Chanukah candle three feet tall? That's right, three feet tall! Well, that's what this story is all about, and it goes like this.

Naftali was a jolly person; he was always so very happy. He knew how important it was to serve Hashem *B'Simcha*, in happiness and joy.

Now, this was all year long, and especially when Chanukah came along he would be more happy than ever before. In fact, in Shul he would be the one to dance right in front of the *Aron HaKodesh*, the holy ark. He would continue to dance and dance, until everyone in the Shul would join in and dance together with him.

One Chanukah, he said to the people of his Shul, "I'm going to explain to you what this dancing is all about. I'll tell you a story, a very strange story indeed, a story that will explain so clearly why I'm so happy on Chanukah.

"It was a few days before Chanukah and I was traveling home to my family. I went to my Rebbe,

Reb Sholom Dov Ber, and asked him for a blessing that I return home safely. For in those days, traveling was quite dangerous, as so often robbers would come along and take everything away.

"The Rebbe blessed me and said, 'Naftali, listen to me. I want you to buy a set of very tall Chanukah candles, at least three feet tall.'

"I asked the Rebbe, 'Three feet tall?'

"'Yes,' came the answer. 'Yes, Naftali. Three feet tall. And may Hashem be with you and protect you.'

"After searching all around town I finally managed to find a set of Chanukah candles three feet tall. I just didn't understand why the Rebbe instructed me to have such tall candles.

"Well," continued Naftali, "the answer came in a few days, for I planned to be home for the first night of Chanukah. Instead, a blizzard broke loose and all of the highways were covered with a heavy blanket of snow. I realized that I would have to spend the first night of Chanukah on the road.

"It was then when it all happened, for all of a sudden a band of robbers appeared and they ordered me out of the coach.

"'Go and say your last prayers,' they said to me in a very harsh voice.

"I pleaded with them and said, 'You may take all of my belongings, but please, let me live!'

"They paid no attention to me. 'Go and say your last prayers,' was the reply.

"Realizing that my life was in danger, and this may be the last time that I light the Chanukah menorah, I climbed up to the top of the wagon while the robbers were so busy packing away all of my belongings. With tears in my eyes I began to recite the blessings for the kindling of the Chanukah menorah, and began to sing *HaNeiros Halalu* as I lit the Chanukah candles.

"It was then that a miracle took place. A miracle from Hashem, the G-d of wonders — a miracle that saved my life!

"For far away, on the top of a tall tower, were firemen. They were looking through a telescope to see if there were any forest fires, and lo and behold, they noticed the flickering flames of the Chanukah menorah.

"Yes," continued Naftali, "These candles were so tall that they could be noticed from such a far distance away.

"It didn't take long and I began to hear the galloping hoof beats of the horses, as the firemen kept coming closer and closer. Upon hearing the hoof beats, the robbers became frightened and called out, 'Run for your lives! Run for your lives! The police are coming. Hurry! Into the forest!.'

"They left everything behind and disappeared into the dark forest. It was then that I realized how fortunate I was in following the Rebbe's advice.

"*Baruch Hashem*, blessed is G-d, a miracle took place and my life was spared.

"You see?" continued Naftali, "This is why I'm so happy on Chanukah. I want to show my thanks to Hashem, the Master of miracles and wonders.

"I want to thank Him for letting me remain alive so that I may again kindle the lovely Chanukah menorah."

The Mountain of Ice

In Europe, there once lived a very great Tzaddik called Reb Meir. He was known to all as the famous Reb Meir of Primishlan. Primishlan was the city where he was Rebbe.

Reb Meir was famous for his great knowledge of Torah and the way he served Hashem so wholeheartedly. People would come to him from all over to learn from him Torah and to receive his *Brachos*, his blessings.

Many times, he would perform miracles just in order to save someone from any danger or harm. And though Reb Meir possessed such great powers, he remained so humble and always tried to avoid being honored and even complimented for his noble deeds.

Now, compared to other cities, the city of Primishlan wasn't a large city at all, yet it had some unusual and outstanding features.

First of all, right in the center of the city there was a very tall and steep mountain. But that was not all; on the very top of the tall mountain was a fountain of flowing water, and since the fountain waters were so sparkling pure and clean, the people of Primishlan decided to build a house right over it and use the sparkling waters of the fountain as a Mikvah in which they would dip themselves and purify themselves each morning before going to Shul to pray to Hashem.

Now, during the summertime, the people would use a stairway which led to the top of the mountain. However, when the winter months came along, these steps could not be used, for they would be blanketed with a coating of ice and snow.

For this reason, a second road was built in order to get to the top of the mountain. It was a winding road that circled the steep mountain, and though it took much more time to get to the top of the mountain, it was much safer to use than the slippery steps that were coated with ice and snow.

Well, you may be surprised to hear this, but of all the people of the city of Primishlan, there was only one who was able to use the steps even during the wintery months. And you can guess who that was, that's right, the Rebbe, Reb Meir himself.

To him, it made no difference whether the steps were clear and dry or covered with a sheet of ice. And no wonder why the people of Primishlan would so often gather around at the foot of the mountain just to marvel at the unbelievable sight as Reb Meir would walk so naturally and so casually up and down on the icy steps without slipping at all.

They would all wonder, "How could such a thing be possible? There surely must be a secret to this."

Now, being such a humble person, Reb Meir paid no attention to all the excitement and just continued on his way.

Well, one day something so very strange happened in the little city of Primishlan, during which Reb Meir finally revealed the secret to the people of his community, and boy were they surprised to find out what that secret really was.

It was on a wintery day when two businessmen traveling on their way home from a distant trip stopped over in the city of Primishlan. The weather was quite difficult for traveling, so they decided to stop off in the city of Primishlan for a few days until the snowy weather will calm down and then continue on their trip home.

Now, the two strangers were in for some surprise, for they didn't realize that the leader of the city of Primishlan was the great Tzaddik and Rebbe, Reb Meir, of blessed memory. And they had never seen a Rebbe before in their life.

They never experienced to be among Chassidim who look up to their Rebbe for guidance and inspiration in order to serve Hashem with all their heart and with all their soul.

And for this reason, they were so puzzled to see how the people of Primishlan displayed so much honor and respect to their leader. They had never in their life seen so much discipline and dedication as they had seen in the city of Primishlan.

It was early the next morning and the two visitors took the winding road that led to the top of the mountain. They were curious to see the Mikvah which stood there. But as they arrived, they noticed a large crowd had gathered to see the spectacle of how their Rebbe, Reb Meir, was about to walk down the ice-coated steps.

It didn't take long and the crowd formed a lane through which their Rebbe, Reb Meir, passed and headed towards the icy steps. And like a miracle right before their eyes, Reb Meir walked down so calmly and so naturally until he reached the bottom of the steep mountain and then headed for his study at home.

To the people of Primishlan, this was a daily experience, but to these two strangers, it was something so unusual.

Now, since they have never seen a Rebbe before, and therefore failed to realize the unusual powers that Hashem gives a Tzaddik, they began to laugh, and said, "If he can do this, so can we!"

The people of Primishlan were surprised to hear this, and before they had a chance to say anything to them, the two young men headed towards the icy steps and called out in laughter, "Heh! So you believe in miracles? Here, we can do the same!"

Saying this, they began taking the very first steps down the icy path. All of a sudden, they began to skid and slip until they lost their balance and kept rolling, over and over until they reached the bottom of the mountain.

Upon seeing this, the people of Primishlan rushed over to help them, for it was quite a dangerous fall.

Gently, they carried the two young men into a nearby home to offer them First Aid. For a few days, they were both aching from bruises and pains all over their body. And even though the two men had shown disrespect to their leader, the Rebbe, the people of Primishlan were so very kind and thoughtful to them.

After a few days of recovery, the two young men were ready to leave for home. Realizing the mistake they had made, that is, to show disrespect to the Rebbe, Reb Meir, they felt it was proper to visit the Rebbe and ask him for forgiveness.

They were so pleased to see how Reb Meir welcomed them so warmly and blessed them. Before bidding farewell to the Rebbe, one of the young men asked Reb Meir, "Could you please explain to me how come you are able to walk on icy steps without slipping?"

Reb Meir smiled and said, "I'll explain it to you. You see, by tying yourself to the One Above, Hashem, the Aibishter, then you will never fall down."

And as Reb Meir said this in Yiddish, *"Az Men Iz Tzugebunden Oiben, Falt Men Nisht Arop Unten.* When one is bound above one cannot fall below."

And Reb Meir concluded, *"Meierel Iz Tzugebunden Oiben, Kon Er Gain Aroif Un Arop, Afilu Oif A Glitchiger Barg.* Meirel is tied to the One Above, that is, Hashem, and therefore he is able to go up and down, even on a slippery mountain."

Yes, the two young men found out that their visit to Primishlan wasn't only to get a rest from traveling, but to learn a very important lesson, a lesson to remember for the rest of their life.

And that is, through learning Torah and through doing mitzvos we bind ourselves and tie ourselves to the One who is above, Hashem Yisborach. And as the Torah itself tells us, *"V'Atem HaD'veikim BaShem Elokaichem, Chayim Kulchem HaYom."* Hashem is the source of all life for those who bind themselves to Him, through learning His Torah and practicing His lovely mitzvos.

The Ten Wedding Gifts

There once lived a very pious and G-d-fearing Jew called Reuven. He was admired by everyone for his unusual kind heart and good deeds. He had no greater pleasure in life than to help anyone who was in need.

Now, Reuven had a hotel which was located at the outskirts of the city, and many travelers would stop off at his hotel for food and rest. After all, the service was truly outstanding, yet the price was set according to how much one could actually afford. So often, he would invite guests who just couldn't afford to pay anything at all. Yes, Reuven was truly a very charitable person.

Now, there were two workers who helped him take care of the guests who would come to the hotel. One was Avraham and the other Sarah. Unfortunately, they were both orphans, that is, they had no father or mother to take care of them.

Reuven took them in as helpers and supported them in a very pleasant and kind way. He knew how great the mitzvah was to be kind to anyone, especially orphans.

Yes, one of the greatest mitzvos is to give a helping hand to those who unfortunately are orphans. There was nothing that Reuven wouldn't do to make life pleasant for both of them. In fact, he treated them as if they were his own children.

As years passed on and Avraham and Sarah were old enough to support themselves, Reuven felt that it was the right time for them to plan their future.

Now, Avraham and Sarah were not related at all, that is, they were not from the same family. And for this reason, Reuven thought it was wise to suggest that they plan their future together.

That's right, that Avraham and Sarah get married and raise a family of their own. And you can imagine how delighted Reuven was to hear that they both agreed. It didn't take long and a date was set for their *Chassuna*, their wedding.

Realizing how great was the mitzvah of *Hachnasas Kallah*, that is, to help and offer support to anyone who is getting married, Reuven said to them, "Here, please do me a favor. Take this purse. You see, there are 600 gold pieces in it. Now, go to the fair, and buy for yourselves all the clothes you need for your wedding day."

At first, they refused to take such a large sum of money from Reuven, but Reuven insisted and they had no other choice but to agree, and off they went to the fair.

As they got onto the coach, Reuven called out, "Remember, make sure to buy the best and nicest outfit for the Chassuna, no matter how much it will cost."

Filled with joy, they left for the fair, thanking Hashem for their unusual fortune and praying that Hashem bless Reuven for his kind heart and good deeds.

Now, as they were traveling towards the fair something so very strange happened — something so very strange indeed!

They noticed an old man sitting on the side of the road crying so bitterly. His hands and feet were tied with heavy chains, and next to him was a very wicked looking officer.

As the old man noticed Avraham and Sarah, he called out, "Help me! Please! Help me! He's taking me away. Please have mercy. Save my life!"

The cruel officer called out, "Stay away from him. There's nothing you can do to help him. Get back onto the road and continue traveling."

"What are you going to do with this old man," they asked. "Why is he crying so bitterly?"

"You heard me," yelled the wicked officer, "Get back onto the road if you want to remain alive!"

The old man kept on pleading, "Help me! Please don't go away. Save my life! I want to live!"

Now, Avraham realized that he has now the chance to do a very, very great mitzvah. Yes, the mitzvah that is called *Pidyon Shevuyim*, to free a Jew who is captured. Bravely, he walked over to the officer and said, "How much money do you want for this old man?"

"Go away!" the officer called out, "You don't have so much money with you. Get back onto the road. Hurry up if you want to remain alive."

Avraham lifted up the purse with the money in it and said, "Please, do tell me, how much money do you want for this old man?"

The puzzled officer looked at Avraham and said, "600 gold pieces and nothing less than that!"

"Very well," said Avraham, "Very well."

Avraham looked at Sarah. There was a moment of silence. Then Sarah shook her head and smiled, "Yes, Avraham. Why of course, go right ahead."

Avraham handed the purse right over to the wicked officer and said to him, "Here. You may count this yourself. You will find all the 600 gold coins in this purse."

The officer just couldn't believe his eyes, for there was exactly that amount in the purse. Quickly, he removed the chains from the old man and said to him, "Go away you old man. You are free. You owe your life to these people. If it were not for them, your life would have been worthless."

Holding the purse tightly in his hand, the wicked officer turned around and ran into the thick forest until he was out of sight.

The old man said to Avraham and Sarah, "I don't know who you are, but I would like you to know that Hashem is surely going to bless you for what you both did today."

Avraham helped the old man onto his wagon and ordered the coachman to bring him back to town so that he may return to his family safely.

After bidding farewell, Avraham and Sarah began their trip back home, that's right, back to Reuven. After all, what's the use of going to the fair now? They are both penniless. They have no money with which to buy anything.

We find Avraham and Sarah standing in front of Reuven. In Avraham's hand was the purse in which Reuven placed 600 gold pieces, but now the purse was empty. Avraham explained to Reuven exactly what had happened, as Reuven listened carefully to the strange and unusual story.

As Avraham finished telling the story to Reuven, Reuven called out in a soft but reassuring voice, "Do you realize how great a mitzvah you both did? Why you both saved the life of that old man! Why that's worth more than all the gold in the whole world."

After saying this, Reuven called over Avraham and Sarah and said to them, "Come, you must be tired and hungry from traveling. Please come, I will give you something to eat."

After the meal, Reuven said, "I want you to know that everything shall proceed just as we planned. You will both travel to the fair and buy for yourselves all the clothes you need for your wedding. And so far as the money is concerned, let me worry about that."

Well, Avraham and Sarah just didn't want to accept any more money from the kindhearted Reuven, but Reuven insisted, and they had no other choice but to agree.

Off they went to the fair, praying to Hashem that he bless Reuven for his kind heart and good deeds.

You can imagine how thrilled Reuven was when Avraham and Sarah returned from the fair and showed him the new outfit of clothing that they bought for their wedding.

Now, realizing how great was the mitzvah to offer help to the one who is about to get married, Reuven decided to invite to the wedding as many people as at all possible. By doing this, he would be bringing that much more joy and happiness to Avraham and Sarah. In fact, he invited all his relatives, his friends, everyone in town was invited to come and join in on the great Simcha.

Finally, the wedding day arrived, and there was so much hustle and bustle in town, as the guests kept arriving from all over to take part in this great and unusual Simcha.

Now, the large hall where the wedding was to take place was filled to capacity as the crowd was waiting anxiously for the arrival of Avraham and Sarah, that is, the *Chassan* and *Kallah*, the bride and groom.

It didn't take long and the crowd burst out with a joyful welcome as Avraham and Sarah finally arrived. There was so much singing and dancing that made everyone so happy and joyful.

Now, outside in the spacious lawn, under the clear sky, the *Chuppah*, the wedding canopy, was all set and ready, that is, the large and beautifully decorated canopy under which the Chassan and Kallah stand during the marriage ceremony. An aisle was formed, through which they were to pass as they head for the Chuppah.

Now everything was set and ready to begin, when all of a sudden something so very strange happened.

As the crowed was hushed to a perfect silence, the large door to the hall was opened and in walked a very holy looking rabbi with a group of ten students following him. Everyone present realized that he must be someone so very special, that is, from his holy appearance, his Shtreimel and long Kapota, the majestic looking fur hat and long overcoat. His red beard, sparkling blue eyes, and radiant face gave him the appearance of a heavenly angel.

Upon seeing this, Reuven went over to the stranger and said, "Welcome to our Chassuna. You have just come on time. I don't know who you are, but I would like you to know that it is certainly an honor for us to have you come and take part in our wedding. But please, do me a favor, please give us the honor in having you recite the blessings, the Brachos under the Chuppah. I'm sure that this will add more joy and delight to the Chassan and Kallah."

Strangely enough, the guest agreed, and everyone went out to the spacious lawn where the Chuppah was set up right under the open skies.

One of the reasons why the Chuppah is set under the open skies is to symbolize that just like there are so many, many stars twinkling and sparkling and shining so brightly in the dark, so we pray to Hashem to bless the Chassan and Kallah that they, too, shall have many, many children who will sparkle so radiantly and bring light to the world through their *Ner Mitzvah V'Torah Or*, through the learning of Torah and practicing the holy mitzvos.

Right after the Chuppah, there was the outcry of Mazal Tov, Mazal Tov, as all the relatives and guests came over to wish the Chassan and Kallah good fortune and blessings.

Everyone joined in forming a large circle to dance around the Chassan and Kallah. After this, everyone returned to the hall where there were rows of tables beautifully decorated and set with an assortment of delicious foods for everyone to eat and enjoy.

Now, during all this time Reuven was trying to figure out who this stranger was. And who are these ten students that came along?

At first, the stranger hesitated to reveal his identity. He felt that it wasn't necessary to tell Reuven his name, but Reuven insisted and begged him, "Please tell me your name. It will add to our Simcha if we will know who you are."

Upon hearing this, the stranger said, "My name is Yisroel Baal Shem Tov, and I have been sent here to bless you and the Chassan and Kallah for your unusual good deeds. Your sincerity and kindness has reached the very Heavens. And the Heavenly Court has appointed us to bless you with good fortune and great success, both in body and in soul."

Well, you can imagine how happy Reuven and the Chassan and Kallah were when they heard this. They felt as if they were the most fortunate people in the entire world.

At the end of the meal, Reb Yisroel Baal Shem Tov stood up and said to the Chassan and Kallah, "I have brought along ten of my students for a special reason. Each one of them is going to leave a gift for both of you to enjoy."

Upon saying this, the first student stood up and said, "I'm going to give you the entire park that is in the center of town. Yes, it's yours for keeps. Make good use of it and truly enjoy it."

Everyone was amazed to hear this. First of all, the park belonged to a very rich and wealthy landowner called the Poritz. And how could the student of the Baal Shem Tov give this away?

Then the second student stood up and said, "Chassan and kallah, I'm going to give you as a gift the large lumber yard that is in the outskirts of the city. It's yours for keeps. Make good use of it."

Avraham and Sarah just couldn't believe what they were hearing. Could this be true? Will they be the true owners of that luxurious park and great prosperous lumber yard? Why, that's a fortune of wealth! And all of this belongs to one Poritz or another!

Reuven, too, was wondering if this was really true. Were they just making believe, or is this really going to happen? He just remained there speechless, silent. He just didn't know what to say.

Well, this went on and on as each of the ten students called out publicly the gift that they were giving to the Chassan and Kallah. And strangely enough, each gift was the property that belonged to one Poritz or another in that town.

After they all announced their gifts, the Baal Shem Tov blessed the Chassan and the Kallah, and Reuven, and all the guests present. Then he prepared to leave.

He said to everyone, "Before I leave I want to say something to you, something I'd like you to remember. I'd like you to know that there is a watchful eye that is forever watching over all of us. It sees all and knows all. Yes, Hashem our Father in heaven, He sees all and knows all and will surely reward in full measure to everyone who learns His Torah and follows the lovely mitzvos. Yes, in due time, all of these ten gifts will surely reach Avraham and Sarah in full measure."

Then, the Baal Shem Tov turned to Reuven and said to him, "Reuven, I want you to know that Hashem will surely bless you and your family with long life and good fortune in return for your kind heart and good deeds."

Quickly, the Baal Shem Tov gathered the ten students and led them to the horse and wagon which stood outside. Strangely enough, there was no coachman to direct the horse, yet as soon as they all entered into the covered wagon something so very strange happened. The horses began to run so speedily and in a cloud of dust and a flash of lightning, off they went until they disappeared into the forest.

Three months have passed, and Avraham and Sarah have already moved into their own cottage which was built near the hotel, where they continued working as they did before.

Kindhearted Reuven helped them buy all the furniture and utensils they needed to make their new home as cozy and comfortable as at all possible.

Every now and then, they would remind themselves about the Baal Shem Tov and the ten gifts that his students gave them during the wedding. But it still remained a mystery, something they just couldn't understand.

Now, everything was going along quite smoothly until one night, when something so very strange happened — something so very strange indeed!

It was a wintery night and a fierce storm broke loose. The winds began to howl through the night as a snow blizzard blanketed the entire village with many feet of snow. It was during the fierce storm when Avraham and Sarah suddenly heard a knocking at the door.

"Who could that be?" they wondered. "Who would be outside during such a fierce blizzard?"

As they opened the door, to their surprise they found a small child, shivering in the bitter cold. He was crying, "Please, oh please, let me in! I'm lost! It's so cold out here. Please let me in!"

"Why, of course," Avraham and Sarah said, "Please, come in!"

Gently, they placed the small child next to the warm fireplace so that he may warm up his hands and feet.

Sarah went to the kitchen and put up some hot water to make a drink for the helpless child. Avraham placed some warm blankets around the child and tried to make him as comfortable as at all possible.

The child opened his eyes and said, "Oh my, you are such kind people. I don't know who you are, but I have never seen such kind people like you before."

Sarah asked the child, "What is your name and where are you from?"

The child looked up and said, "My name is Brewster, and I live in a large mansion right at the end of this forest.

"You see," continued the child, "each night my father orders one of the servants to take me horseback riding in the forest, and tonight something went wrong. A heavy snow blizzard came along and we just lost each other. I was following his horse as closely as possible as we were heading for home. But the fierce winds came along and I just couldn't see where I was going. Luckily, I noticed your cottage and headed towards it."

"You know, if I would have to stay outside in that bitter cold any longer, I don't think I would have made it. You saved my life! Yes, you really saved my life."

Avraham prepared a comfortable bed for little Brewster. He was so tired and exhausted, and it didn't take long, and he fell fast asleep.

Avraham said to Sarah, "As soon as the storm will quiet down and the roads will be cleared from the drifting snows, we will be able to bring Brewster back to his home. His parents surely must be worried. They must be looking for him."

"I feel so sorry for them," Sarah added, "If they only knew that their little Brewster is so safe, tucked so comfortably under a heavy and warm blanket and is so fast asleep, this would make them so happy. But, alas, we must wait until the storm passes."

Avraham looked at Sarah and said, "You also must be tired by now, good night Sarah." After which Sarah answered, "Good night Avraham."

Now, the Poritz had already started the search for his lost son. He sent out an alarm and plea for everyone to join in and help him find little Brewster who was lost in the forest during the fierce snowstorm. As the hours passed, and there was no trace or sign of little Brewster, the Poritz wondered if he will ever see him again.

Little Brewster was his one and only child, and he was so dear and precious to him. The Poritz was ready to give away anything he owned in return for his lost son. How little did he know that Brewster was so safe and sound, enjoying the loving and tender care of the kindhearted Avraham and Sarah.

And you can imagine how surprised the Poritz is going to be when, lo and behold, in came Avraham and Sarah holding onto the hands of little Brewster!

As the roads were finally cleared from the heavy drifting snows that blanketed them during the fierce storm and blizzard, Avraham and Sarah prepared little Brewster for his trip back home. He just couldn't wait to get back to his dear, but worried parents.

And you can imagine how surprised Brewster's parents were when he finally returned home so safe and sound. Brewster told his parents the strange story that had happened to him the day he got lost, and how Avraham and Sarah saved his life.

"I owe my life to these two people," Brewster called out, "They saved my life and they were so kind to me. They are so nice and such kindhearted people."

"Very well," called out the Poritz, "Very well. I will make sure that they will be rewarded for this in full measure."

Upon hearing this, Avraham called out, "Oh no! Please, not at all. I deserve no reward. After all, what I did is what the Torah teaches, *"V'ohavta L'rai-acha Ko-mocho,"* to love your fellow man just as much as you love yourself. I did what Hashem commanded me to do, and so far as the reward, let Hashem take care of that."

But the Poritz paid no attention to Avraham's words and said, "No, my dear friend. I must reward you for saving the life of my one and only child."

Well, the Poritz decided to celebrate, "I'm going to make a royal banquet and invite all of my noble friends to come and join in on this day of festivity. And you, Avraham and Sarah, you will be my guests of honor."

Avraham and Sarah had no other choice but to accept his invitation. They were wondering if this royal banquet had anything to do with the ten strange gifts promised to them on the day of their wedding by the students of Reb Yisroel Baal Shem Tov.

Well, it didn't take long. There was so much hustle and bustle in town. So many dignified and royal guests were arriving from all over, and of course every Poritz in town came to take part in this grand celebration.

As soon as all the guests were seated, the Poritz stood up and said, "I want you all to know how thankful I am to Avraham and Sarah for saving the life of my one and only child. And in return for such a noble deed, I'm going to reward them with an unusual gift, a gift I think they truly deserve. I'm going to give them full ownership of the spacious park that is located in the center of town. It's all yours, Avraham and Sarah. May it bring you much joy and happiness, as much as you have brought us today."

Upon hearing this, another Poritz stood up and said, "And I will give you the entire lumber yard which is located in the outskirts of the city."

Well, you can easily guess what happened next, that's right, as one Poritz finished announcing his reward, another Poritz stood up and announced his reward, until all of the ten gifts promised by the students of Reb Yisroel Baal Shem Tov were presented to Avraham and Sarah, exactly as the Baal Shem Tov himself assured them.

Yes, the blessings of Reb Yisroel Baal Shem Tov and his students have finally reached Avraham and Sarah in full measure, in return for their kindhearted good deeds.

How strange are the ways of Hashem Yisborach, who sees all and knows all and rewards everyone in full measure for serving Him with all their heart and with all their soul.

The Lost Letter

Here is a story that happened many years ago, a story that has an important lesson for all of us today. It happened in the time of the great rabbi called Reb Yisroel Baal Shem Tov, of blessed memory.

The Baal Shem Tov served Hashem so devotedly, with *Mesiras Nefesh*, self sacrifice, and in return for this, Hashem gifted him with a special great power, that is, the power to give a *Bracha*, to bless anyone who was in need. People would come from all over to visit him and receive his heavenly blessings.

Now, this story happened during the very last days of the Baal Shem Tov, right before he passed away. He called all of his students to his bedside and blessed them. Each student paid close attention to every word that their Rebbe said to them, realizing that this may be the final Bracha, the last blessing right before he will pass away.

Of all the students there was one who was called Reb Laibel. Reb Laibel was a very devoted follower of his Rebbe, the Baal Shem Tov. Laibel was a very wealthy businessman. In fact, he was the richest person in town. He owned many factories, shipyards, spacious farmland, and many lumberyards. Of course, Laibel was so very charitable too. He always gave Tzedakah so generously to all who turned to him for help. Now, Laibel was also blessed with a large family, and everyone was in the best of health.

Laibel thought to himself, I don't have to ask my Rebbe for any Bracha, for I have everything. There is nothing that is missing. There is nothing to ask for. I am already blessed with everything.

Well, Reb Laibel decided not to ask for a Bracha, and this of course was such a mistake, a very big mistake indeed. For even though he was so fortunate and prosperous at that moment, he failed to realize that the wheel of fortune is forever turning and no one knows what tomorrow may bring.

And it is for this reason that we pray each and every day and ask Hashem, our Father in heaven, to continue to grant us life, good health, and good fortune.

It didn't take long and Reb Laibel was called to the bedside of his master, the Rebbe, Reb Yisroel Baal Shem Tov. Yes, it was his turn to see his Rebbe. And could you imagine what happened when he told the Rebbe that he needs no Bracha at all!

Upon hearing from Reb Laibel, that he asks for no Bracha, the Baal Shem Tov thought for a moment, I must teach him a lesson, a lesson he will remember for the rest of his life.

"Well, my dear student," he said. "If there is nothing I can do for you, perhaps there is something you can do for me."

Upon hearing this, Laibel called out, "What can that be, Rebbe? What can that be? I am ready and willing to do anything for you."

The Baal Shem Tov asked for a blank piece of paper upon which he wrote a letter, signed his name at the bottom, and then placed it into an envelope and sealed it so very securely. Then he looked up to Reb Laibel and said, "Please take this letter and give it to Reb Sholom and make sure that he gets it as soon as possible. Also be very careful that only Reb Sholom reads this letter."

"Why of course." said Reb Laibel. "I'll be glad to bring it to him." Saying this, he bid farewell to the Rebbe and left the room.

Reb Laibel was so thrilled to know that he had the honor of doing a favor for his Rebbe, the great Reb Yisroel Baal Shem Tov. But how little did he know that he was in for a big surprise, for something so very strange was about to happen, something that was to serve as a lesson for Reb Laibel, a lesson to remember for the rest of his life.

As Reb Laibel was traveling home, a fierce storm broke loose and there was a very heavy downpour of rain. The winds were howling and the roads became so muddy, making traveling so very difficult. Finally, he arrived at the mansion in which he lived. He stopped off at the hallway where he bent over to remove his boots which were soaking wet and covered with a thick layer of mud. And it was then when it all began.

For as he bent over, the sealed envelope containing the letter which he was to bring to Reb Sholom slipped out of his pocket and fell under a large wooden closet which stood in the hall.

Now, Reb Laibel didn't notice this at all and strangely enough, as soon as this happened, Reb Laibel forgot all about the sealed envelope and the letter written by Reb Yisroel Baal Shem Tov.

Oh my! How awful! Now what's going to happen? Well, something so very strange is going to happen to Laibel — something so very strange indeed! For a few days later, early in the morning, there came a knocking at the door. As he opened the door, a messenger brought him a letter to read. As he opened the letter and read it, he called out, "Oh my! Oh why that's impossible!"

Laibel called over Miriam, his wife, and said to her, "Look at this letter that I received today. Look what's written in it. One of my factories caught on fire and burnt down to the ground. All the people were luckily saved, but the factory is a total loss. Oh my! Why did this happen?"

His wife Miriam comforted him and said, "Why should this bother you, Laibel? After all, this is only one of the many factories that you own. Remember, you're still the richest man in town."

"You're so right, Miriam. Yes, you're so right. I'm not going to let this bother me at all." Reb Laibel continued on with his daily routine, trying to forget the tragedy of the factory that burnt down to the ground.

Now, a few months have passed, and alas, again there came a knocking at the door. As Laibel opened the door, there stood a messenger with a telegram for him.

"Oh, not again!" Laibel cried out. "Not again!" as he read the telegram to his wife, Miriam.

"What are you going to say now? Look what's written here: there was a fierce storm and lightning struck a row of tall trees in my largest forest and alas! All the trees caught fire and burnt down to the ground. Oh my, how awful!'"

But again, Miriam his devoted wife calmed him down saying, "But Laibel, remember, you still own so many shipyards and farmlands. You're still the richest man in town."

Well, it didn't stop at that. Unfortunately, the very same thing happened six months later and again a year later. Slowly but surely, all the wealth and fortune that Laibel had began to disappear as one tragedy followed another.

Many times Laibel would stop and ask himself, Why is this all happening to me? What did I do to deserve this? I surely must have done something wrong. What could that be? If I would only know! Yes, if I would only know I would correct it immediately.

Well, little did Laibel realize how wrong he was in not asking for a Bracha from the Baal Shem Tov so many years ago. True, at that time, he was so fortunate and so prosperous. Yet, it was so important for him to be blessed by his great and holy rabbi, Reb Yisroel Baal Shem Tov, for a blessing from anyone and especially a blessing from a Tzaddik, a very holy person, that goes a long way in extending the period during which Hashem sends good fortune and prosperity in full measure.

Yes, a Bracha from a Tzaddik opens a new channel through which we can receive so much more of *Kol Tuv*, all that is so very good, both for our body and for our *Neshama* too, our soul. So this is the great mistake that Laibel did, and ten years have already passed and lo and behold, things kept turning from bad to worse!

Realizing that his entire fortune had disappeared totally, he had to sell all his jewelry and silverware just in order to have enough food for his family to eat. Laibel realized finally that he even must sell his expensive furniture just in order to survive, to have food on the table.

Well, we're now in for such a big surprise. For the very first piece of furniture Laibel decided to sell was the very large wooden closet that stood in the hall. It was made out of solid cedar wood, and it was worth a lot of money.

Now, as the moving men were carrying out the closet from the hall, it was then when it all began. For there on the floor was the lost letter.

Remember? That's right! The letter that the Baal Shem Tov wrote ten years ago, right before he passed away. You can imagine what happened as Laibel took a look at the lost letter. As he bent down to pick it up, what thoughts flashed through his mind at that moment? There he stood, motionless, holding on tightly to the sealed envelope.

His wife looked at him and said, "Laibel, what's the matter? And what's that you're holding in your hand? Why is your face paled with fright? Please tell me. What happened, Laibel? Please tell me."

Well, Laibel was truly speechless. He just didn't know what to say, for in his hand was the secret to all the strange things that had happened to him for the past ten years. Yes, the secret to the unfortunate past and the key and solution that will bring him once again a very bright future.

Reb Laibel told his wife that he's going to take a trip to Reb Sholom who lived quite a distance away and hand over the lost letter.

He said to his wife, "After all, the Baal Shem Tov asked me to bring it to him and make sure that he reads it. I have no other choice but to do exactly that. True, ten years have already passed, and how could I ever explain to Reb Sholom all that had happened until now? Yet, I must carry out my Rebbe's wish."

His wife bid him farewell and off he went to bring the lost letter to Reb Sholom.

Now, Reb Sholom was one of the wealthiest people of his city. He was so very prosperous and was blessed with a fortune of wealth. He lived in the outskirts of the city in a large spacious mansion. It was surrounded with a beautiful park, decorated with dazzling flower

beds and colorful orchards and gardens, and countless birds of all colors, flying and chirping about so
merrily. Truly, a sight to behold.

As Reb Laibel came close to the mansion, he was
greeted by a guard who was standing at the gate,
"What is your name please?"

"My name is Reb Laibel, an old friend of Reb
Sholom, and I have a letter for him."

The guard said, "Very well. Give it to me and I will
see that he will read it."

"Oh no!" Reb Laibel cried out. "Heavens forbid! I
must give this letter to him myself."

But the guard refused to let Reb Laibel enter into
the gates leading to the mansion. Upon seeing this,
Reb Laibel said, "Then would you be so kind and tell
Reb Sholom that there is someone who has a very
important letter for him."

"Very well." said the guard. "And by the way, may
I tell him who wrote the letter?"

Reb Laibel thought for a moment and then said,
"Well, to tell you the truth, this may sound so very
strange, but believe me, it's true."

"What do you mean by that?" asked the guard.

"You see, this letter was written by the great rabbi,
Reb Yisroel Baal Shem Tov, of blessed memory."

"What?" called out the guard. "The Baal Shem Tov? Why he passed away ten years ago! How could that be?"

Reb Laibel pleaded, "Please believe me. It's true! Please tell this to Reb Sholom. He will surely understand."

"Very well."

The guard agreed and went to tell Reb Sholom about the stranger and the sealed envelope.

The guard told Reb Sholom exactly what Reb Laibel asked him to say. Upon hearing this, Reb Sholom said, "There's only one way to find out if this is true. Bring me the letter and I will read it. After all, he was my Rebbe. And I am fully acquainted with my Rebbe's handwriting."

"But Reb Sholom," said the guard, "He refuses to give it to me. He claims that the Baal Shem Tov ordered him to give it to you himself. So he asks to be permitted to give it to you."

"Very well," said Reb Sholom. "Very well. Let him in."

Well, get ready for a big surprise! For as Reb Laibel entered into the room he immediately recognized his old *chaver*, his old friend, Reb Sholom. But Reb Sholom didn't recognize him at all, for he was dressed in torn and shabby clothing.

Slowly, Reb Laibel walked over to Reb Sholom and said to him, "Reb Sholom, I have a letter for you. The letter is from the Baal Shem Tov. He asked me to give it to you."

Reb Sholom just couldn't believe what he was hearing. Curiously, Reb Sholom took the envelope and examined it carefully. And then he called out excitedly, "Why it's true! It's true! The seal on this envelope is the seal of my Rebbe, of blessed memory."

Slowly, Reb Sholom opened the sealed envelope and took out the letter.

There were a few moments of absolute silence as Reb Sholom read the letter word for word. Suddenly, tears appeared in his eyes as he looked up to Reb Laibel and said, "Why it's you, Reb Laibel! I just can't believe this! Where have you been all these years? Oh my! It's so hard for me to believe that this is the same Reb Laibel I knew ten years ago!"

Reb Sholom wiped the tears from his eyes, put his arm around Reb Laibel and said, "Reb Laibel, I want you to know that your troubles are over. You have had enough. You have surely learned your lesson by now. Here, I will explain this to you. I will read this letter to you."

"Dear Reb Sholom, ten years have already passed since Reb Laibel was instructed to bring this letter to you. He failed to realize the importance of a Bracha, a blessing. And he paid for this mistake in full measure. Now, Reb Sholom, I turn to you, my dear student. Please set him back on his feet once again. Give him all he needs to get back into business and Hashem will surely bless you for this."

Well, you can imagine how shocked Reb Laibel was when he found out what was written in the letter, especially when he noticed that the date written at the top of the letter was the very same date of the day he brought the letter to Reb Sholom!

Yes, there is so much that we can learn from such an unusual story. It teaches us how important it is to be blessed, that is, to be blessed by anyone, and especially by a great Tzaddik, a very righteous man like the Baal Shem Tov, of blessed memory.

The story also teaches us the unusual powers that Hashem gives to those who serve Him truthfully, through the study of His holy Torah and the practice of His holy mitzvos.

The Forbidden Road

Our Sages tell us, *"Lo Hamidrash Ha-ikar, Ela Ha-Maaseh,"* though the learning of Torah is so very, very important, what counts most is action.

That's right, he main thing is not only to learn Torah, but to do all in your power to bring all of your knowledge and learning into action, by being good to your fellow man and to always display good character.

One of the many important rules our Sages teach us is self-control. This means to be patient and never lose your temper. That's right, it's so very wrong to lose your temper. In fact, our Sages tell us, *"Kol HaKoes Ke-ilu Oved Avodah Zara.* Anyone who loses his temper and becomes angry is equal to the one who worships an idol."

And the story you are about to hear is about a person who failed to realize the importance of this rule, and would so often become angry and lose his temper. And one time, as a result of this, he got himself into a lot of trouble.

There once lived a very wealthy person called Reb Beryl. He owned many large factories, lumberyards, and ships that sailed the seas. He was really worth some fortune of wealth.

Now, though Reb Beryl had all he needed in order to live a comfortable and luxurious life, there was something that he was missing so badly, and that was good character.

He was known to be so very selfish. He would hardly give any Tzedakah, any charity, willingly. And in addition to this, he was a *Baal Gaavah*, a show-off. He would always brag about his riches and wealth whenever he had a chance to do so.

Surprisingly, Reb Beryl was a very learned man, for he spent much of his youth in learning Torah. But it seems that Reb Beryl did not succeed in Maaseh, that is, to turn all of his knowledge into good action. And to top it off, Reb Beryl was a very impatient person. He would so often become angry and lose his temper.

You see, Reb Beryl was so very successful in gaining so much wealth and fortune for himself, but was so very, very poor and failing when it came to good character.

Now, in the town where Reb Beryl lived there was no Yeshiva, so he hired a private tutor, Reb Laibel the Melamed, to come to his house and teach his son Dovid.

Every now and then, Reb Beryl would come into the room where Reb Laibel the Melamed and his son Dovid would be learning Torah and listen to the lesson.

One day, Reb Beryl heard the melamed say to his son Dovid, "To be rich, or to be poor, is entirely in the hands of Hashem. No rich man can be sure that he will be rich forever, and no poor man must remain poor for the rest of his life, for in one moment the richest man could become penniless, and the poor man can become so very rich."

Upon hearing this, Reb Beryl became so angry, he lost his temper and called out, "How dare you teach him such a thing. Why that makes no sense at all! You may leave my house, and don't bother to come back again."

Without saying a word, Laibel the Melamed got up and left the house.

Dovid began to cry, "Father! Why did you do this? Why did you send him away? He was such a good teacher, I really liked him. Please call him back!"

But Dovid's father paid no attention to him at all. He was so very angry. Yes, angry enough to lose his temper and send away Dovid's teacher from his house.

Upon seeing Dovid cry, Reb Beryl got up and left the house, and as he got outside, he began to walk and walk, not even paying attention to where he was going. He just wanted to have some fresh air in order to calm down before coming back home again.

But something so very strange happened to Reb Beryl. Something that taught him a lesson, a lesson to remember for the rest of his life.

In the distance, he noticed a police officer walking towards him. As the officer came close enough, he called out, "You are under arrest. Come with me to the police station."

Reb Beryl didn't understand. "What's the meaning of this? What wrong did I do? Why are you arresting me?"

"Ah, don't look so innocent. You know that you are not allowed to be on this street on Sunday!"

Saying this, the officer took out a piece of paper and said to Beryl, "Now you have a choice of one of these two, either sign this paper and you may go back home, or come with me to the police station."

Reb Beryl was so confused, he was really mixed up and didn't realize what was happening. As the officer handed him a pen he signed his name at the bottom of the paper.

"Thank you," said the officer, with a vicious smile on his face. "Thank you. My superiors are going to be quite proud of what I did today."

"What do you mean by that?" asked Reb Beryl.

"You see," answered the officer, "You have just now signed away all of your property to the government. You are now penniless, you don't even own the shirt that is on your back."

Saying this, the officer turned away and headed back for his office to announce the good news to his superiors. But Reb Beryl remained there alone, motionless, as if he had just been in a nightmare. "I just can't believe it! I just can't believe it!"

The rich and prosperous Beryl is now penniless and it all happened in just one moment.

"Hey, wait! Oh my! Isn't that what the teacher taught my son Dovid? That the richest person could become penniless in just one moment. Oh my!

"What can I do now? And how can I return home? How can I ever tell this to my family? Oy, I don't know what to do. I just don't know what to do."

Well, you see, Reb Beryl lived in a town where Jewish people were forbidden to walk on certain streets on Sundays. And if they would be found on any of those forbidden streets, they would be punished severely, that is, they would have to turn over all of their properties and wealth to the government.

Yes, Reb Beryl was not as fortunate as we are today, to live in a country where we can enjoy total freedom to learn Torah and practice all of its mitzvos.

But in the town where Reb Beryl lived, there was no such freedom at all. And alas, now Reb Beryl is in real trouble. What is he going to do now? How can he return home? How can he face his son Dovid and tell him what had happened?

Well, it was then that Reb Beryl finally realized how wrong it was for him to lose his temper and to send away the teacher from his house.

Not having enough courage to go home right away, Beryl decided to go to his Rebbe and tell him the whole story and hear what the Rebbe has to say. Perhaps he will be able to help him. Perhaps the Rebbe will show him a way how to correct the mistake that he had made.

The Rebbe said to Beryl, "I want you to realize that in order that Hashem may help you, you must change your ways. You must be kindhearted and be willing to share your own fortunes with others who are not as fortunate as you."

"You see, Reb Beryl," continued the Rebbe, "The only reason why Hashem blessed you with riches is only to give you the blessed opportunity to give Tzedakah, charity, to the poor and needy. So the more Tzedakah you will give, the more Hashem will continue to bless you with riches and prosperity.

"Now you have a chance to begin from anew. I want you to take upon yourself to give away *Maaser*, that is, one-tenth of all of your money for Tzedakah, charity. And as you will do this, I will pray to Hashem to help you and free you from your present unfortunate situation."

"But Rebbe, I don't understand. How can I make a promise to give one-tenth of all my moneys to Tzedakah if I am now penniless. I signed away all of my property and money to the government."

"Never mind," answered the Rebbe, "Never mind. You just do what I say and Hashem will surely bless you with success."

Beryl promised to the Rebbe to give away one-tenth of all his money to Tzedakah and then said to the Rebbe, "And what will be now?"

The Rebbe smiled and said, "Beryl, you can now go home and pray to Hashem. I will do the same. After all, Hashem is a G-d of miracles."

The Rebbe led Beryl to the door and bid him farewell.

As Reb Beryl came home he told his wife all what had happened and said, "Come, let's take the Tehillim, the book of Psalms, and pray to Hashem to help us in this moment of need."

Well, while Reb Beryl and his wife were pouring out their heart to Hashem, as they both recited the holy portions of the Tehillim, something very strange took place in the house of the officer who had the paper upon which Beryl signed his name to give away all of his property and money to the government.

You see, the officer decided to celebrate a little before bringing the good news to the government, so he took out a tall bottle of wine and began to drink to his heart's content and he just continued drinking, glass after glass, until he became so drunk that he just fell fast asleep, sitting by the table.

Little did the officer realize that he was crumpling the paper upon which Reb Beryl's signature was placed, and as he fell asleep he dropped the paper on the floor.

Meanwhile, the housemaid came in and noticed the officer snoring away on the tables. She called out, "How can I do my house cleaning with him around?"

Nevertheless, she took the broom and began sweeping the floor. As she finished sweeping up the floor, she took all the trash that was on the floor and threw it into the blazing fireplace. Of course, this also included the crumpled paper with Reb Beryl's signature on it.

Well, the Rebbe's blessings reached Reb Beryl in full measure, for a miracle indeed did take place, and Hashem answered the prayers of the Rebbe and the Tehillim recited by Reb Beryl and his wife.

And you can imagine what happened when the officer awoke and just couldn't figure out what happened to the paper. He was afraid to tell this to the government for they would surely punish him for being so clumsy, so he kept it a secret and never told anyone about it.

Well, little Dovid was so happy to find out that his melamed Reb Leib was called back again to teach him Torah, for Reb Beryl apologized to Reb Leib and asked him for his forgiveness.

"Please continue teaching my son the wonderful words of Torah," said Beryl, "It is now that I realize how true are the words of the holy Torah."

Of course, Reb Beryl kept his promise and distributed a vast amount of money for Tzedakah which was yet only a tenth of what he actually owned.

Yes, Reb Beryl surely learned a lesson, a lesson he is going to remember for the rest of his life, and that is what is written in the Torah, *Aser T'aser*, one must give one-tenth of his earnings to Tzedakah.

And as our Sages tell us, *Aser Bishvil Shetis-asher*, that is, the true path to prosperity is through giving Tzedakah generously, for the more you give, the more Hashem blesses you in return, for your good deed.

The Missing Wallet

Little Dovid was paying close attention to all what his teacher was telling him in class. "Remember," said the teacher, "In case you ever find anything, you must do all in your power to find out who the owner is and return it as soon as possible. By doing so, you will be fulfilling the great mitzvah of *Hashovas Avaida*, the returning of a lost article. And remember, if you fail to return it but keep it instead, this is just as if you are stealing."

All the way home from school, little Dovid kept on thinking of how the Torah tells us the importance of being honest and the great reward that is due to the person who fulfills the mitzvah of Hashovas Aveida, the returning of a lost article. Yes, Little Dovid was a well-mannered child and above all he wanted to be honest, that's right, just the way the Torah teaches.

All of a sudden, something so very strange happened, for Dovid's thoughts were interrupted as he noticed something lying in the middle of the sidewalk.

As he came closer he called out, "Oh my! Look what I found! Oh boy, now I have the great mitzvah of Hashovas Aveida, the mitzvah to return an article that is lost."

Quickly, Dovid bent over and picked up a wallet filled with money. As he opened the wallet, he wanted to see if there was any identification card inside so he will know to whom to return the wallet. While looking for the card, Dovid just couldn't help noticing the large sum of money in the wallet.

Carefully, he counted the bills. And to his surprise, there were twelve one-hundred dollar bills.

"Gosh!" he exclaimed, "Twelve hundred dollars in cash, what a fortune of wealth!"

And it was then that it all began, for Little Dovid's *Yetzer Tov*, the inner voice that tells us to do good things, told him, "Return the money to the owner. The Torah says you must return it. It's a mitzvah. If you keep it, it will be stealing..."

Then the Yetzer Hara, the inner voice that tells us to do bad things, would come out and say, "Dovid, you need that money! There are so many things you can do with that money. There are so many good things you could buy with that money. Come on, now's the chance to be rich!"

But at that very moment, the Yetzer Tov called out, "Dovid, you learned in school today that you must return a lost article. It's such a great mitzvah! Remember Dovid, Hashem's watching. Hashem is waiting to see what you are going to do next."

Well, this quarrel between the Yetzer Tov and the Yetzer Hara continued for quite a while as Little Dovid stood there with this wallet in his hands.

"Look Mommy!" yelled excited Dovid, as he came rushing into the bedroom where his mother was resting from an illness. "Look what I found!" he said excitedly as he handed his mother the large wallet. His mother was quite amazed to see such a large sum of money.

"Oh, here is an identification card," Mother said. "It reads: First National Bank, Mr. Green, President. My, that's the large bank at the corner of our street," said Mother. "Oh, if we only had half of that money we would be able to do so many things. We would be able to call the family doctor and pay for the medicines so that I might be cured from my illness. We could buy new clothes, too, instead of wearing old and torn clothing," his mother said.

Dovid and his mother kept on thinking of all the wonderful things that they could buy with the money.

All of a sudden, Dovid called out, "How useless it is for us to sit back and think of the things we could do with the money that doesn't belong to us. We can't use this money anyway."

His mother listened as Dovid explained to her all about what he learned in the Yeshiva that morning, how the Torah teaches us to be honest and to return anything that we may find.

"Why of course," his mother assured him. "We are not going to keep this money. *Chas V'Shalom*, G-d forbid. That would be like stealing. Now, I want you to go over to the bank at the corner and ask for Mr. Green. Tell him that we found his wallet and if he can identify it we will gladly return it to him. Explain to him that since there is so much money in the wallet, I'm afraid to let you carry it in the street. So, I will hold it until he arrives and identifies the wallet."

Filled with excitement, Little Dovid hurried over to the bank and went over to the information desk and asked, "May I please see Mr. Green?"

The man at the desk was quite surprised to see a little boy ask for the president of the bank. "You see," continued Dovid, "he lost something and I found it."

"Just one moment please," said the man at the desk as he picked up the phone and called for the president.

The clerk asked Dovid to follow him as he walked towards the president's private office. Dovid entered and explained to Mr. Green how he found the wallet on the way home from school that day and that he gave it to his mother to hold until the owner would come and identify it.

"Very well," said Mr. Green. "I'll take you home in my own car." Dovid had the thrill of his lifetime as he rode in the president's luxurious automobile.

All the way home, Dovid explained to Mr. Green what he learned in the Yeshiva that day and how lucky he felt to be able to do the mitzvah of Hashovas Aveida, to return the lost article to its original owner.

Mr. Green was very impressed with all what Dovid was telling him. Dovid told Mr. Green that his father passed away when he was yet a year old, leaving nothing for his mother to support the family.

"Oh, I'm so sorry to hear this," said Mr. Green. "How unfortunate."

A few moments later, Little Dovid called out, "Look, there's my house!" as he pointed to an old run down house.

All the children playing in the street were quite surprised to see that their friend Dovid was riding in such a fancy car. They all gathered around to greet him as he stepped out of the fancy car.

Mr. Green followed Dovid up the squeaky staircase that led to his apartment.

"Mother, here is Mr. Green from the bank. He came to identify the wallet that I found."

"May I enter?" asked Mr. Green in a gentle tone.

"Why certainly," said Mother. "Please, sit down and make yourself comfortable. You see, Mr. Green, I am a very sick woman and the doctor said that I may not leave my bed. Please forgive me for not being able to offer you better hospitality."

"Oh, that's all right," answered Mr. Green, as he pulled over a chair and sat down right down next to the bed. "I want you to know that you have a wonderful boy. I have been quite impressed by his honesty, his cleverness, and sincerity. He's an excellent example of a real Yeshiva boy," said Mr. Green.

"I'm really proud of my little Dovid. He is all that I have," said his mother as she began to cry.

"Tell me more about your family and yourself," said Mr. Green.

At first, she hesitated to tell him the bitter story of her life, but Mr. Green insisted and she began to unfold a very interesting but unusual story.

"You see, Mr. Green," said Dovid's mother, "At one time, we were so very wealthy. My husband, may he rest in peace, had a very large business. He gave a lot of Tzedakah, a lot of charity, and always helped the poor and needy.

"However, when my husband took sick all of a sudden, he was unable to attend the business. A year later, he died. I had to sell the business at a fraction of its value.

"Years passed and there was no income at all. All that we had to live on was the little money that was left from the business. Now, we are penniless. Were it not for the money I receive from my charitable friends, I wouldn't have any money with which to support little Dovid and myself."

As Dovid's mother reached for a handkerchief to wipe the tears from her eyes, Mr. Green sat there and thought for a while. Suddenly he asked, "By the way, what is your name? Your family name?"

"My name is Goldberg. And my husband's name was Avraham."

Upon hearing this, Mr. Green stood up and said, "Wait a minute. Are you and your late husband from the city of Kreslovska?"

"Why, yes, Mr. Green. We are from the city of Kreslovska. How do you know?"

Mr. Green stood there motionless, he just had nothing to say. He put his head down and began to cry bitterly.

Dovid and his mother were shocked to see Mr. Green, the president of the bank, crying. They looked on, wondering, but said nothing.

After a few moments of absolute silence, Mr. Green raised his head and explained to Mrs. Goldberg the reason for his sudden outburst of crying.

He told them that he too once lived in the city of Kreslovska. He was so very poor and could hardly manage to support his family.

One day, he met Mr. Abraham Goldberg who was a wealthy businessman. After explaining to Mr. Abraham Goldberg his hardships, Mr. Goldberg generously gave him a large sum of money with which he was to start a small business. It didn't take long and Mr. Green's business kept on growing larger and larger and brought in a large fortune of wealth.

"When I borrowed the money from Mr. Goldberg, I promised to repay him the entire sum plus a sizable share in his business. But strangely enough, Mr. Goldberg didn't want to accept any thanks for loaning the money to me. He kept on saying, Never mind, it's a great mitzvah, *Baruch Hashem* that I'm able to help you.

"Nevertheless," continued Mr. Green, "I kept on putting aside the sizable share which I promised to Mr. Goldberg for his loan. The amount put aside amounts to eighty thousand dollars. You see, Mrs. Goldberg, during the last war I lost contact with your husband and I have failed to find out where he was.

"*Baruch Hashem*, now I have finally been fortunate in finding you, Mrs. Goldberg. I'm sorry to hear that you've lost your husband. He was such a fine person."

Mrs. Goldberg just couldn't believe her ears, and Dovid jumped for joy.

"*Baruch Hashem*! Hashem has finally answered our prayers. Now we can call the doctor and pay for the medicines so that you may be well again," Dovid said to his mother.

"Oh thank Hashem for His kindness," sighed a relieved Mrs. Goldberg. "Now we can pay back all the money that we owed to the Yeshiva. They have been so kind to us all this time."

"It gives me such a wonderful feeling," said Mr. Green, "to know that I can finally pay off my debt to your family for all that your husband has done for me in the time of need.

"Now, the first thing we have to do is to cure you from your illness. I have a wonderful doctor whom I will send to you as soon as I return to my office. I am sure that with the help of Hashem, he will be able to make you feel well again.

"Mrs. Goldberg, your worries are all over now," continued Mr. Green. "You now have enough money to buy a new house for yourselves and the share that you still have in my business will be more than enough for you to pay for all your daily expenses."

"Oh boy!" called out Little Dovid. "Now I can buy a new set of *Chumashim* and a *Shulchan Aruch* too!"

"Even more than that," said Mr. Green. "Now you can buy yourself a complete library of all the Seforim and holy books that you may ever need."

Cheerfully, Mrs. Goldberg returned the wallet to Mr. Green, as he got ready to leave for the office.

Upon returning to the school the next day, Dovid told all his friends the wonderful thing that had happened to him.

"It all happened because I did what my Rebbe told me to do, that is, to return anything you may find to its original owner," said Little Dovid.

To this, his Rebbe added, "Yes, the Torah brings us wealth and fortune, both in this world and also in the World to Come."